QUESTION[illegible]

AS/A-Level

Pure Mathematics

Robert Smedley

Philip Allan Updates
Market Place
Deddington
Oxfordshire
OX15 0SE

tel: 01869 338652
fax: 01869 337590
e-mail: sales@philipallan.co.uk
www.philipallan.co.uk

ISBN 0 86003 769 X

Printed by Raithby, Lawrence & Co Ltd, Leicester

P00073

Contents

Introduction

■ ■ ■

Questions and answers

Introduction

About this book

This book provides typical examination questions from the pure mathematics component of AS and A2 mathematics specifications. It comprises ten sections, each containing AS and A2 questions; the questions within each section get progressively more difficult. The table below gives guidance on the levels for the questions in each section. However, you should check your specification as there are differences between exam boards.

Section and topic	Questions for AS	Questions for A2
(1) Algebra	1, 2, 3	4
(2) Functions	1, 2	3, 4
(3) Coordinate geometry	1, 2	3
(4) Sequences and series	1, 2, 3	4, 5
(5) Trigonometry	1, 2, 3, 4	5, 6, 7, 8
(6) Exponentials and logarithms	1, 2	3
(7) Differentiation	1, 2, 3, 4	5, 6, 7, 8
(8) Integration	1, 2, 3, 4	5, 6, 7, 8, 9
(9) Numerical methods	1	2, 3, 4
(10) Vectors		1, 2

You can attempt the questions yourself as part of your revision. For each question, two solutions are given, accompanied by an examiner's comments. The first solution is by a student who can expect a low grade (candidate A) and the second is by an A-grade student (candidate B).

The examiner's comments indicate the number of marks that would be awarded for the candidate's solution together with details of why marks have been awarded and lost. For example, sometimes marks are awarded for the method used, even though the candidate's answer is incorrect. The examiner's comments highlight good practice as well as poor practice, so you can learn from the two candidates' examples.

It is suggested that you attempt the question first without looking at either of the solutions given. Then compare your solution with those of candidates A and B, and use the examiner's comments to judge how many marks your solution would gain.

Candidate A's solutions

It is worth noting a number of characteristics of candidate A's solutions. Try to avoid these yourself.

You will notice that candidate A:

- tends to use standard formulae
- tends to use decimals, even for questions giving clues in the wording, such as 'leave your answers in surd form'
- is careless with $+/-$ signs and expanding brackets, for example $-1(x + y) = -x + y$ or $(x + 3)^2 = x^2 + 9$
- is not precise in writing mathematical statements, for example writing $f(x) = 1 + 3x - 6x^2$ when it should be $f(x) \approx 1 + 3x - 6x^2$ (polynomial approximation)
- does not analyse the structure of the questions to find out what the examiner wants. For example, if the first part of a question asks for something to be expressed in a particular way, this candidate answers the second part of the question, ignoring what has been shown in the first part. Remember that the questions have been carefully structured to help you answer all parts.
- does not finish questions; for example, in a question asking for the coordinates of a point, this candidate only finds the x-coordinate

Candidate B's solutions

Candidate B's solutions are not perfect, but are typical of an A-grade candidate. Try to learn from these.

You will notice that candidate B:

- tends to use what is easiest and not necessarily standard formulae. This can save time.
- explains the solution to the examiner; for example, he/she numbers equations when they are referred to further on in the solution
- makes statements that indicate knowledge; for example 'at the turning point, the gradient is 0, so put $\frac{dy}{dx} = 0$'
- ensures that sufficient steps are included in any workings, so the examiner can award marks for working up to the point of an error
- does not use decimals unless (i) the question asks for an approximation or (ii) the decimal being used is exact
- draws very clear sketch graphs and includes all the required information

Common errors

Looking at the solutions of both candidates, you will notice that careless errors result in the loss of marks — in some cases, a significant number of marks. Some of the most common errors and misconceptions are included in the solutions provided, to assist you in identifying your own weaknesses. They include:

- squaring out brackets as $(x + 3)^2 = x^2 + 9$, which is not true

- using the square root function inaccurately; for example $\sqrt{\sin^2 x - \cos^2 x} = \sin x - \cos x$, which is not true
- dropping negative signs when dealing with brackets and substitution. For example, in evaluating $f(-1)$ where $f(x) = x^3 - 2x^2 + x$, $f(-1) = (-1)^3 - 2(-1)^2 + (-1) = -1 - 2 + 1$, which is not true.
- multiplying only one side of an equation by a constant, in order to clear a fractional term. For example,

  $$4 - \frac{x}{3} = x - 2$$

  Multiplying by 3 gives

  $$3 \times 4 - 3 \times \frac{x}{3} = x - 2$$

  i.e. $12 - x = x - 2$

  The correct result from multiplying by 3 is $12 - x = 3(x - 2)$.
- simplifying fractions incorrectly, for example $\frac{2 \pm 3\sqrt{5}}{2} = 1 \pm 3\sqrt{5}$, which is not true
- $\ln\left(\frac{p}{q}\right) = \frac{\ln p}{\ln q}$, which is not true.
- If $e^k = 3$ then $k = \frac{3}{e}$, which is not true.
- $\cos(\theta + 30°) = \cos\theta + \cos 30°$, which is not true.
- $\int \sin^2 x \, dx = \frac{\sin^3 x}{3} + c$, which is not true.

As you revise, make a list of the common errors you make, together with any you notice when going through the questions in this book. Your own personal list will help you to focus and eliminate incorrect practices.

General exam guidance

- Read the question carefully and make sure that you are using the correct information.
- Read the question carefully and note how many decimal places/significant figures the examiner is asking for.
- Read the question carefully and note whether the examiner wants an exact answer. For example, the question may state 'show that $x = \sqrt{5}$', indicating that x is to be left as a surd and not given as a decimal.
- When reading the question, ask yourself *why* the examiner has structured it in the way it is presented. The longer questions usually contain parts that follow on from each other, using results from previous parts.
- Do not waste time trying to achieve 1 additional mark when there are still other questions on the paper that you haven't attempted. Remember that the first parts of questions tend to be easier than the final parts.

- Do not cross out your attempt at a question if you are unable to replace it. The examiner will go through your attempt looking for correct methods and calculations. Remember that the examiner wants to award you marks, not take them away.
- Carry out some simple checks to see if your answer makes sense. For example, substitute answers to simultaneous equations back into the equations to make sure they satisfy them all.
- Check that you have used all the information given in the question and do not make assumptions. For example, you cannot assume that an angle is 90° simply because it looks about 90° on your sketch.
- In examinations where formulae booklets are provided, make sure that you are familiar with what is included and what is not included in the formulae book.
- Learn the formulae you need.

I hope you enjoy tackling these questions and that the book helps you achieve success in your mathematics AS/A-level. The best of luck!

Robert Smedley

Algebra

Question 1

(a) Express $y = x^2 - 4x + 1$ in the form $(x + a)^2 + b$, where a and b are constants to be determined. (3 marks)

(b) Hence, sketch the graph of $y = x^2 - 4x + 1$ and state the minimum value of y. (3 marks)

Answer to Question 1: candidate A (3 out of 6 marks)

(a) $y = (x - 2)^2 - 3$

This candidate has expressed y in the correct form, for 3 marks.

(b)

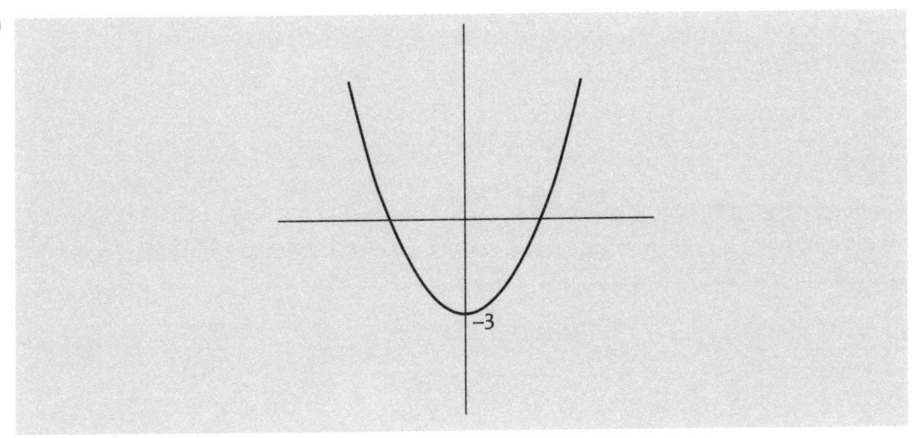

The minimum value of y is 3.

This sketch graph is incorrect. The graph of $y = (x - 2)^2 - 3$ does not have the y-axis as a line of symmetry. The candidate has shown -3 on the sketch, which is the correct minimum value, but is not the y value at which the correct curve intersects the y-axis. The candidate has failed to state -3 as the minimum value and the axes are not labelled. No marks are awarded.

Answer to Question 1: candidate B (6 out of 6 marks)

(a) $y = (x - 2)^2 - 3$

The correct form gains full marks.

(b)

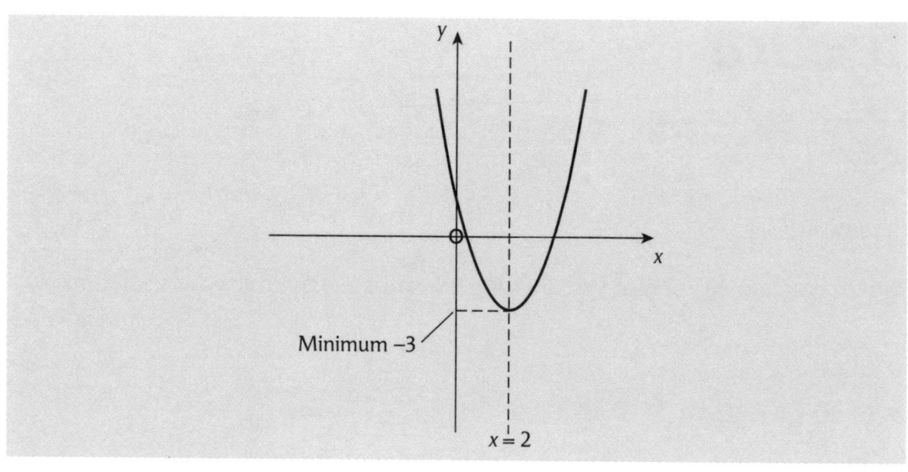

The minimum value of y is -3.

The sketch graph shows the line of symmetry clearly and the coordinates of the minimum turning point. The candidate has clearly stated the minimum value of y as -3, which is correct. 3 marks are awarded.

Question 2

(a) Sketch, on the same set of axes, the graphs of $y = |3x - 1|$ and $y = x^2 + 1$, stating clearly the coordinates of any points where the graphs meet the axes.

(3 marks)

(b) Solve the equation $|3x - 1| = x^2 + 1$. (4 marks)

■ ■ ■

Answer to Question 2: candidate A (4 out of 7 marks)

(a)

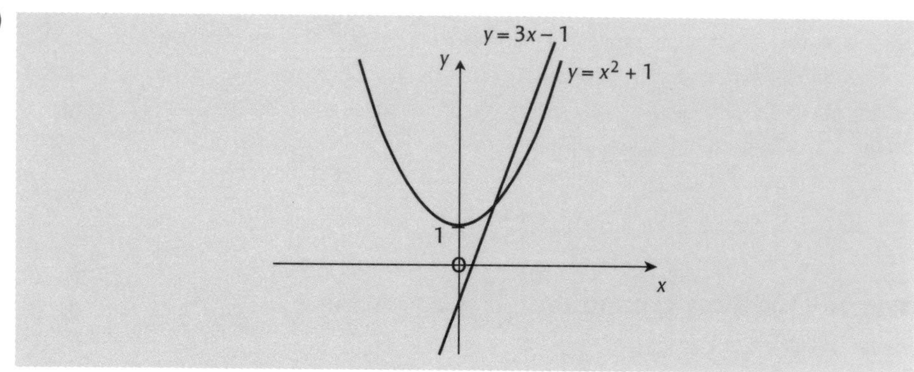

This sketch gains 2 of the 3 marks. $y = x^2 + 1$ is correct and the candidate has sketched $y = 3x - 1$ correctly, but ignored the modulus sign.

(b)

$$3x - 1 = x^2 + 1$$

$\therefore \quad x^2 - 3x + 2 = 0$

$\therefore \quad (x - 2)(x - 1) = 0$

$\therefore \quad x = 2 \text{ or } x = 1$

Again, the candidate has ignored the modulus sign and consequently has only found two solutions out of four, for 2 marks.

Answer to Question 2: candidate B (5 out of 7 marks)

(a)

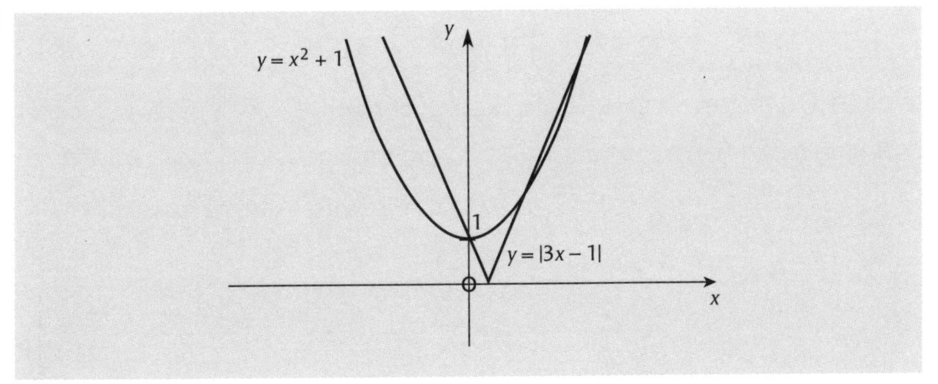

This is a good, clear sketch graph, for 3 marks, which shows $y = x^2 + 1$ and $y = |3x - 1|$ correctly.

(b) There are two possibilities:

$$3x - 1 = x^2 + 1$$

$\therefore \quad x^2 - 3x + 2 = 0$

$\therefore \quad (x - 2)(x - 1) = 0$

$\therefore \quad x = 2 \text{ or } x = 1$

or

$$-3x - 1 = x^2 + 1$$

$\therefore \quad x^2 + 3x + 2 = 0$

$\therefore \quad (x + 2)(x + 1) = 0$

$\therefore \quad x = -2 \text{ or } x = -1$

Although this candidate has taken account of the two possible cases, a slip with a minus sign has resulted in the second set of solutions being incorrect. The mistake occurred at the initial stage, writing $-3x - 1$ instead of $-(3x - 1) = -3x + 1$. The candidate should have noticed that the sketch graph intersection points do not agree with their own solution. 2 marks are awarded.

Question 3

(a) Determine the values of k for which the quadratic equation

$$(k + 1)\,x^2 + 4kx + 9 = 0$$

has equal roots. (4 marks)

(b) Solve this equation in the case when $k > 0$. (3 marks)

■ ■ ■

Answer to Question 3: candidate A (5 out of 7 marks)

(a) $k = 1$ gives $2x^2 + 4x + 9 = 0$, which doesn't factorise and so doesn't have equal roots.

$k = 2$ gives $3x^2 + 8x + 9 = 0$, which doesn't factorise and so doesn't have equal roots.

$k = 3$ gives

$$4x^2 + 12x + 9 = 0$$

$$(2x + 3)\,(2x + 3) = 0$$

$$x = -\frac{3}{2} \text{ or } -\frac{3}{2}$$

(b) This has equal roots.

e This candidate has taken a non-standard approach to this question and used trial and error. In this case, it has resulted in finding one correct value of k, but the question asks for *values*. This solution gains 2 marks for the $k = 3$ case. As the value of k found is the positive one and the resulting quadratic has been solved, the candidate gains full marks for part (b) of the question.

■ ■ ■

Answer to Question 3: candidate B (7 out of 7 marks)

(a) For equal roots, the discriminant has to equal 0:

i.e. $b^2 - 4ac = 0$

$\therefore$ $(4k)^2 - 4(k+1) \times 9 = 0$

$\therefore$ $16k^2 - 36k - 36 = 0$

i.e. $4k^2 - 9k - 9 = 0$

$$(4k + 3)(k - 3) = 0$$

$$\therefore \quad k = -\frac{3}{4} \text{ or } k = 3$$

e The candidate has considered the discriminant of the quadratic and generated the two possible values of k. This is correct and a good solution for 4 marks.

(b) When $k = 3$

$$4x^2 + 12x + 9 = 0$$

i.e. $$(2x + 3)(2x + 3) = 0$$

$$\therefore \quad x = -\frac{3}{2}$$

e The candidate then uses the positive k value and correctly finds the root of the resulting quadratic, for 3 marks.

Question 4

(a) Express as a single fraction in its simplest form

$$\frac{(x + 3)(x - 5)^2}{(x + 2)(x - 1)} - \frac{(x + 3)}{(x - 1)^2}$$ (2 marks)

(b) Show further that the numerator of the single fraction can be expressed in the form

$$Ax^4 + Bx^3 + Cx^2 + Dx + E$$

where A, B, C, D, E are constants to be determined. (3 marks)

■ ■ ■

Answer to Question 4: candidate A (1 out of 5 marks)

(a) $$\frac{(x + 3)(x - 5)^2}{(x+2)(x - 1)} - \frac{(x + 3)}{(x - 1)^2} = \frac{(x + 3)(x - 5)^2(x - 1)^2 - (x + 3)(x + 2)(x - 1)}{(x + 2)(x - 1)(x - 1)^2}$$

e This candidate has expressed the difference as a single fraction, but not in its simplest form. The simplest common denominator is $(x + 2)(x - 1)^2$, as $(x - 1)$ is a common factor in both denominators. 1 mark is awarded.

(b) Now,

$$(x + 3)(x - 5)^2(x - 1)^2 - (x + 3)(x + 2)(x - 1)$$

$$= (x + 3)(x^2 + 25)(x^2 + 1) - (x + 3)(x^2 + x - 2)$$

$$= (x + 3)(x^4 + 26x^2 + 25) - (x^3 + 4x^2 + x - 6)$$

$$= x^5 + 26x^3 + 25x + 3x^4 + 78x^2 + 75 - x^3 - 4x^2 - x + 6$$

$$= x^5 + 3x^4 + 25x^3 + 74x^2 + 24x + 6$$

In the expansion and simplification of the numerator, the candidate has expanded $(x-5)^2$ and $(x-1)^2$ incorrectly, ignoring cross terms, which is a common error. Note that $(x-5)^2 = (x-5)(x-5) = x^2 - 10x + 25$. This candidate should have noticed that the answer required (as indicated in the question) is a polynomial expression of degree 4, not degree 5. This answer fails to score any marks.

■ ■ ■

Answer to Question 4: candidate B (5 out of 5 marks)

(a)

$$\frac{(x+3)(x-5)^2}{(x+2)(x-1)} - \frac{(x+3)}{(x-1)^2} = \frac{(x+3)(x-5)^2(x-1)-(x+3)(x+2)}{(x+2)(x-1)^2}$$

$$= \frac{(x+3)(x-1)(x^2-10x+25)-(x^2+5x+6)}{(x+2)(x-1)^2}$$

$$= \frac{(x^2+2x-3)(x^2-10x+25)-(x^2+5x+6)}{(x+2)(x-1)^2}$$

$$= \frac{(x^4-8x^3+2x^2+80x-75)-(x^2+5x+6)}{(x+2)(x-1)^2}$$

$$= \frac{x^4-8x^3+x^2+75x-81}{(x+2)(x-1)^2}$$

Comparing the numerator with $Ax^4 + Bx^3 + Cx^2 + Dx + E$ gives $A = 1, B = -8, C = 1, D = 75$ and $E = -81$.

This candidate has chosen the simplest common denominator and simplified the numerator correctly. The solution is clearly presented with all the steps shown. (5 marks)

Functions

Question 1

The functions f and g are defined on the domain of all real numbers by $f(x) = x - 3$ and $g(x) = 5 - x^2$.

(a) Sketch the graphs of $y = f(x)$ and $y = g(x)$ on separate axes. (2 marks)

(i) Only one of the functions f, g has an inverse. Identify which has an inverse. For the function that has an inverse, explain why and find the inverse function. For the function that does not have an inverse, explain why not. (4 marks)

(ii) State whether g is odd, even or neither. (1 mark)

(b) Find

(i) $fg(x)$

(ii) $gf(x)$ (3 marks)

Hence find the value of x for which $fg(x) = gf(x)$. (2 marks)

■ ■ ■

Answer to Question 1: candidate A (4 out of 12 marks)

(a)

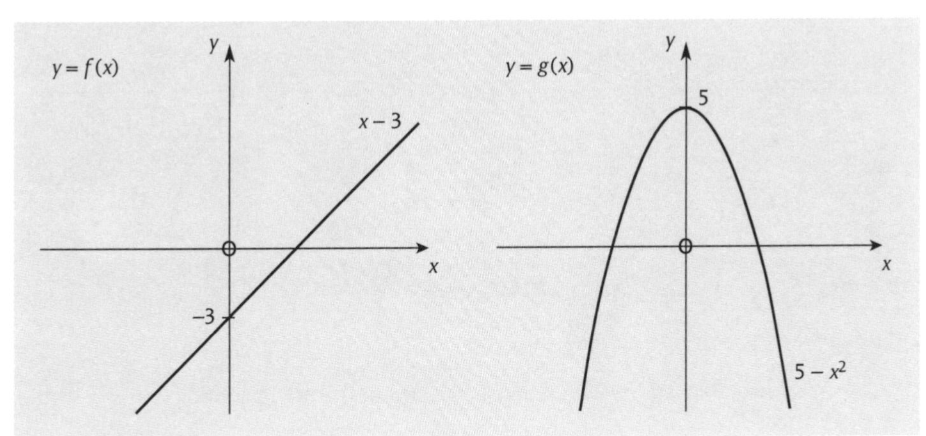

The sketch graphs are correct, for 2 marks.

(i) Function f has an inverse. The inverse is $x + 3$.

The candidate has correctly identified f as the function that has an inverse, for 1 mark. In addition, the candidate has given the inverse of f correctly. Although the candidate has not written $f^{-1}(x) = x + 3$, the answer gains 1 mark. However, the candidate loses 2 marks by failing to explain why f has an inverse and g doesn't.

(ii) Odd

e This is incorrect. g is even, which you can tell from its symmetry about the y-axis.

(b) (i) $fg(x) = (x - 3)(5 - x^2)$

$= 5x - x^3 - 15 + 3x^2$

(ii) $gf(x) = (5 - x^2)(x - 3)$

$= 5x - 15 - x^3 + 3x^2$

They are the same.

e In (i) and (ii), candidate A has interpreted $fg(x)$ to mean $f(x) \times g(x)$, and $gf(x)$ to mean $g(x) \times f(x)$, rather than the composite functions fg and gf respectively. No marks are awarded.

■ ■ ■

Answer to Question 1: candidate B (11 out of 12 marks)

(a)

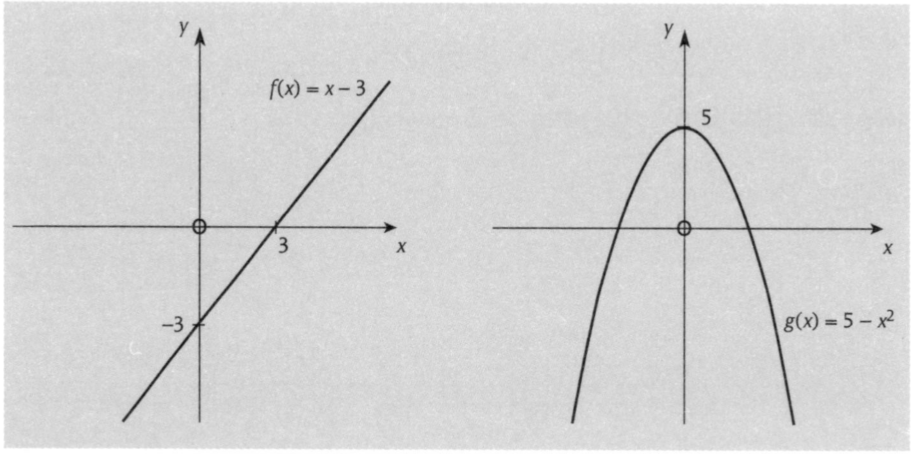

e Both sketch graphs are correct, for 2 marks.

(i) The function f has an inverse because it is a one-to-one function.

$f^{-1}(x) = x + 3$

e f is the function with an inverse (1 mark). The candidate explains why f has an inverse but not why g does not, for 1 mark out of 2 (g is not one-to-one on the domain of all real numbers). The inverse $f^{-1}(x) = x + 3$ is correct, for a third mark.

(ii) g is even because its graph is symmetrical about the y-axis.

The function g is even, for 1 mark. The candidate also explains how he/she has identified this property from the graph — but this was not required by the question.

(b) (i) $fg(x) = f(5 - x^2)$

$= 5 - x^2 - 3$

$= 2 - x^2$

(ii) $gf(x) = g(x - 3)$

$= 5 - (x - 3)^2$

$= 5 - (x^2 - 6x + 9)$

$= 6x - x^2 - 4$

If $fg(x) = gf(x)$ then

$$2 - x^2 = -x^2 + 6x - 4$$

$$\therefore \quad 6x = 6$$

$$\therefore \quad x = 1$$

The candidate has answered this part of the question correctly and presented the solution clearly, for 5 marks.

Question 2

The portion of the graph of $y = f(x)$ for $0 \leqslant x \leqslant 3a$ is sketched below.

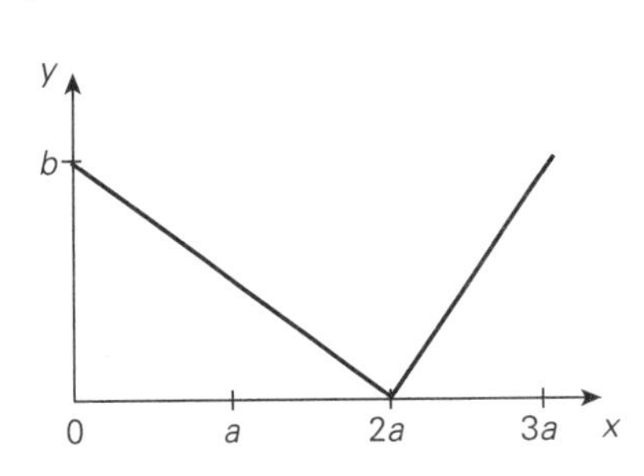

(a) Sketch the graph of

(i) $y = f(x + a)$ for $0 \leqslant x \leqslant 2a$ (2 marks)

(ii) $y = f(2x)$ for $0 \leqslant x \leqslant a$ (2 marks)

(b) Given that f is an even function, sketch the graph of $y = f(x)$ for $-3a \leqslant x \leqslant 3a$. (2 marks)

Answer to Question 2: candidate A (4 out of 6 marks)

(a) (i)

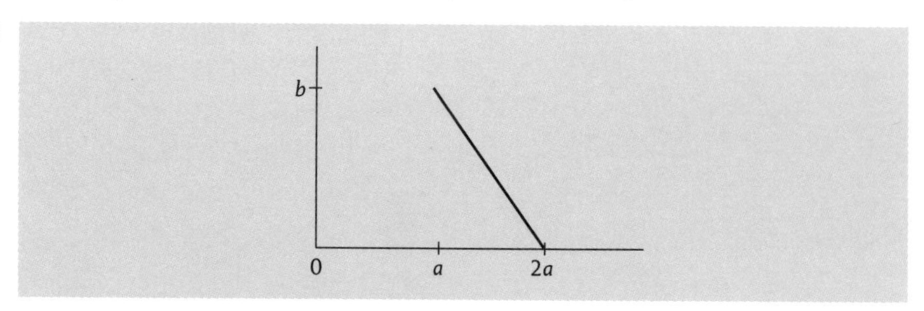

This is incorrect. It seems that the candidate has interpreted $f(x + a)$ as a translation of a units in the positive x-direction for $f(0) = b$, but then failed to use this interpretation correctly for $f(2a)$. There are no labels on the axes.

(ii)

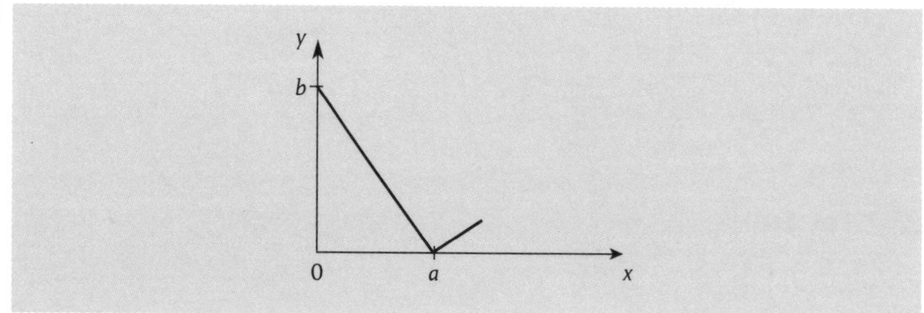

The candidate has also sketched part of the graph for $x > a$, which was not required, but the section for the required interval $0 \leqslant x \leqslant a$ is correct, for 2 marks.

(b)

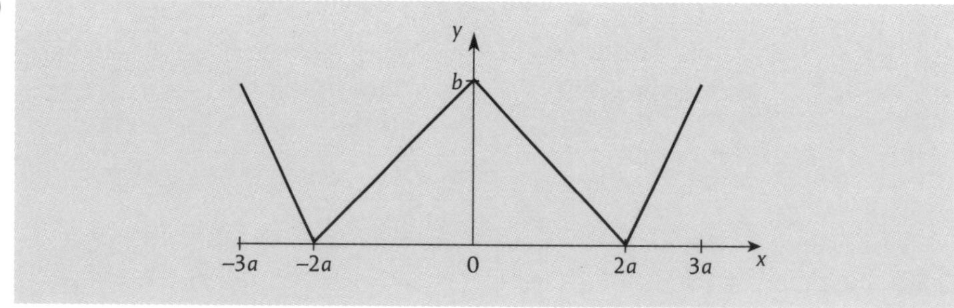

This is correct, for 2 marks.

Answer to Question 2: candidate B (6 out of 6 marks)

(a) (i)

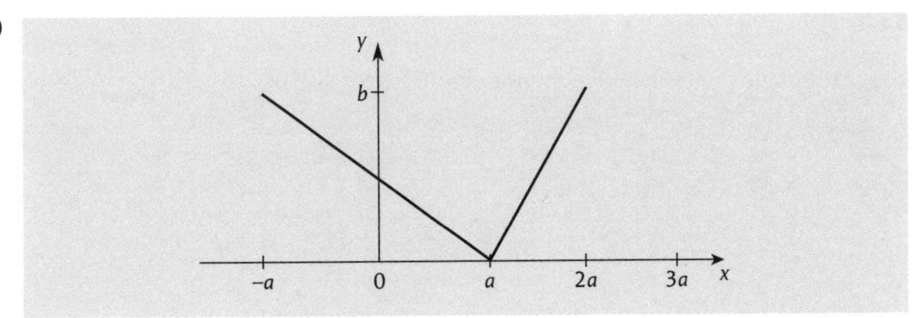

This candidate has sketched the graph for $-a \leqslant x \leqslant 2a$ rather than the interval specified in the question, $0 \leqslant x \leqslant 2a$. However, the sketch is correct for the required interval, for 2 marks.

(ii)

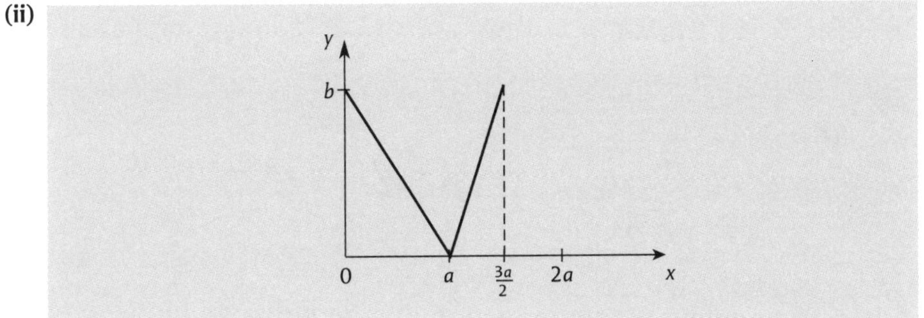

This is a correct sketch of the graph for the interval required, $0 \leqslant x \leqslant a$, for 2 marks. Once again, this candidate has gone beyond the requirements of the question and gains no extra marks for this.

(b)

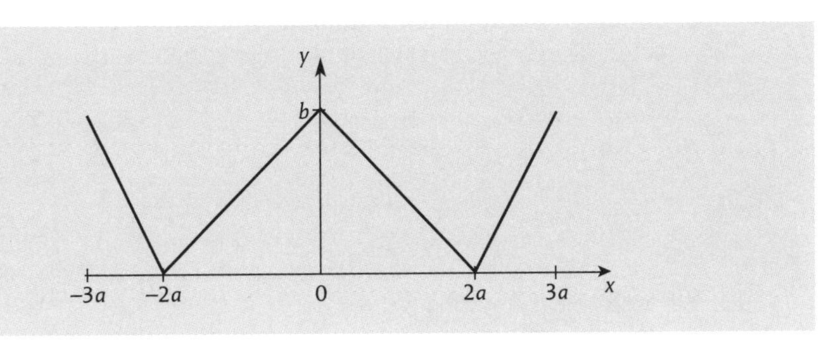

This is correct, for 2 marks.

Question 3

$f(x) = 2x^3 - 7x^2 - 5x + 4$

(a) Show that $f(4) = 0$ and hence state a linear factor of $f(x)$. (2 marks)

(b) Express $f(x)$ as a product of three linear factors. (2 marks)

(c) Solve the inequality $f(x) < 0$. (3 marks)

■ ■ ■

Answer to Question 3: candidate A (3 out of 7 marks)

(a) $f(4) = 0$. A linear factor is $(x - 4)$.

> This candidate has simply re-stated $f(4) = 0$, which is given in the question, without showing the substitution. However, the linear factor is correct, for 1 mark.

(b) $f(x) = (x - 4)(Ax^2 + Bx + C)$

$= Ax^3 + Bx^2 + Cx - 4Ax^2 - 4Bx - 4C$

$= Ax^3 + Bx^2 - 4Ax^2 + Cx - 4Bx - 4C$

Comparing with $f(x)$ gives $A = 2, C = -1$. Therefore, $B = 1$.

So

$f(x) = (x - 4)(2x^2 + x - 1)$

$= (x - 4)(2x - 1)(x + 1)$

> Candidate A has used an unnecessarily long method of comparing coefficients to find the correct quadratic factor. It would have been easier to find the quadratic factor by inspection. The linear factors are correct, so the candidate gains full marks. However, the method used would waste time in the exam.

(c) If $f(x) < 0$, then

$(x - 4)(2x - 1)(x + 1) < 0$

$$x < 4, x < \tfrac{1}{2}, x < -1$$

> This method for solving the inequality is incorrect as it does not take account of all possible cases. No marks are awarded.

Answer to Question 3: candidate B (6 out of 7 marks)

(a) $f(4) = 2(4)^3 - 7(4)^2 - 5(4) + 4 = 0$
A linear factor is $(x - 4)$.

The candidate has shown clearly the calculation required to evaluate $f(4)$ by substituting into $f(x)$. The linear factor $(x - 4)$ is correct. 2 marks are awarded.

(b) $f(x) = (x - 4)(2x^2 + x - 1) = (x - 4)(2x - 1)(x + 1)$

This is a correct factorisation of $f(x)$, for 2 marks.

(c) Sketching the graph of $y = f(x)$:

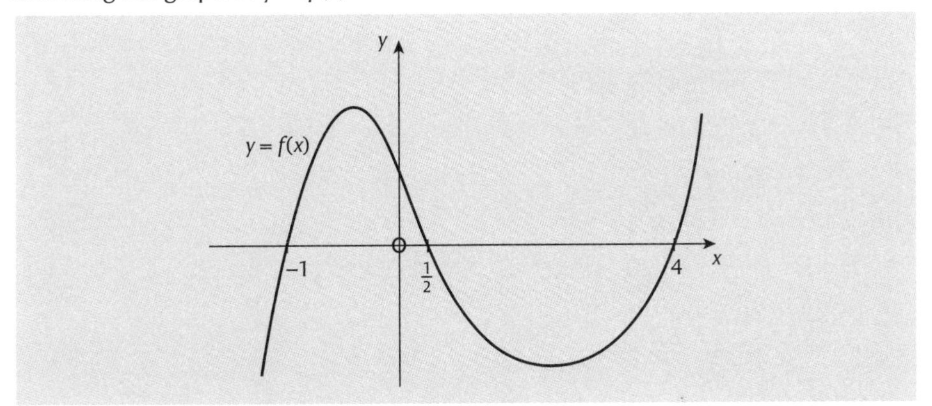

We want $f(x) < 0$, i.e. where the graph lies below the x-axis.

From the graph, the graph is below the x-axis when $\frac{1}{2} < x < 4$.

The sketch graph is correct, as is the explanation of how to identify when $f(x) < 0$, but this candidate has failed to recognise that $f(x) < 0$ when $x < -1$ as well as when $\frac{1}{2} < x < 4$, so only 2 of the possible 3 marks are gained here.

Question 4

The function f is defined as

$$f(x) = \frac{ax + b}{x - 1}, \quad x \neq 1$$

(a) Given that $f(0) = 1$ and $f(2) = 7$, find the values of the constants a and b. (2 marks)

(b) Find the range of f. (2 marks)

(c) Find $f^{-1}(x)$, where f^{-1} denotes the inverse of f, and state the domain of f^{-1}. (3 marks)

(d) Show that the x coordinates of the points where the graphs of f and f^{-1} intersect satisfy the equation

$$x^2 - 5x + 1 = 0$$ (3 marks)

Answer to Question 4: candidate A (3 out of 10 marks)

(a) $f(0) = \dfrac{b}{-1}$, so $b = -1$.

$f(2) = \dfrac{2a + b}{2 - 1}$, so $2a + b = 7$. Therefore, $a = 4$.

e This is correct, for 2 marks, but the mathematical statements could be more clearly presented.

(b) The range is the same as the domain, i.e. $x \neq 1$.

e This is incorrect as the domain and range are not the same.

(c)

$$y = \frac{4x - 1}{x - 1}$$

$$x - 1 = \frac{4x - 1}{y}$$

$$x = \frac{4x - 1}{y} + 1$$

$$\therefore \quad f^{-1}(x) = \frac{4x - 1}{x} + 1$$

e This candidate has clearly started with $y = \frac{4x - 1}{x - 1}$ and made an attempt to rearrange for x. Unfortunately, the candidate has failed to collect all x terms together. No marks are awarded.

The domain of f^{-1} is the same as the range of f.

e This is correct, for 1 mark.

(d) Where the graphs of f and f^{-1} intersect,

$$\frac{4x - 1}{x - 1} = \frac{4x - 1}{x} + 1$$

i.e. $$x(4x - 1) = (x - 1)(4x - 1) + 1$$

$$\therefore \quad 4x^2 - x = 4x^2 - 5x + 2$$

$$\therefore \quad 4x = 2$$

$$x = \tfrac{1}{2}$$

e The candidate has used the incorrect inverse from **(c)** and then manipulated it incorrectly. No marks are awarded.

■ ■ ■

Answer to Question 4: candidate B (9 out of 10 marks)

(a) $f(0) = \dfrac{b}{-1} = 1 \Rightarrow b = -1$

$$f(2) = \frac{2a - 1}{1} = 7 \Rightarrow a = 4$$

$$\therefore \quad f(x) = \frac{4x - 1}{x - 1}$$

e This is correct, for 2 marks.

(b) Rearrange for x:

$$y = \frac{4x - 1}{x - 1}$$

$$\therefore \quad y(x - 1) = 4x - 1$$

$$\therefore \quad yx - y = 4x - 1$$

$$\therefore \quad yx - 4x = y - 1$$

$$\therefore \quad x(y - 4) = y - 1$$

$$\therefore \quad x = \frac{y - 1}{y - 4}$$

The range of f is $\{x \in \text{ set of reals}, x \neq 4\}$.

e This is correct, for 2 marks. An alternative method for finding the range would be to sketch the graph.

(c) From the rearrangement,

$$f^{-1}(x) = \frac{x - 1}{x - 4}$$

e This is correct, for 2 marks, but the candidate has missed the final part, i.e. stating the domain of the inverse function. The domain of f^{-1} is the same as the range of f.

(d) The two graphs intersect at points on the line $y = x$. Therefore, put $y = x$:

$$\frac{4x - 1}{x - 1} = x$$

$$\therefore \quad 4x - 1 = x^2 - x$$

$$\therefore \quad x^2 - 5x + 1 = 0$$

e This is a good, clear answer, for 3 marks.

Section 3

Coordinate geometry

Question 1

(a) Find the equation of the line l passing through the points A(–1, 4) and B(–2, 6).

(3 marks)

(b) Given that l intersects the x and y axes at points P and Q respectively, state the coordinates of P and Q. (2 marks)

(c) Find the length of PQ, leaving your answer in surd form. (2 marks)

■ ■ ■

Answer to Question 1: candidate A (6 out of 7 marks)

(a) Using the equation for a line,

$$y - y_1 = \left(\frac{y_2 - y_1}{x_2 - x_1}\right)(x - x_1)$$

$$\therefore \quad y - 4 = \left(\frac{6 - 4}{-2 + 1}\right)(x - (-1))$$

$$\therefore \quad y - 4 = -2(x + 1)$$

$$\therefore \quad y = -2x + 2$$

e This candidate uses correctly the formula for a straight line passing through two points, and gains full marks.

(b) When $x = 0, y = 2$. P is $(0, 2)$.

When $y = 0, x = 1$. Q is $(1, 0)$.

e Unfortunately, this candidate interchanges P and Q by mistake, but uses a correct method for finding the coordinates of the intersection points with the axes and is awarded 1 mark.

(c) $\text{PQ} = \sqrt{(0 - 1)^2 + (2 - 0)^2}$

$= \sqrt{5}$

e The distance PQ is calculated correctly, using the formula for finding the distance between two points, for 2 marks.

■ ■ ■

Answer to Question 1: candidate B (7 out of 7 marks)

(a) The gradient of AB is

$$m = \frac{6 - 4}{-2 + 1} = -2$$

The line l has equation $y = -2x + c$. The line passes through A$(-1, 4)$, so

$$4 = -2(-1) + c$$

$$c = 2$$

The equation of l is $y = -2x + 2$.

e The equation for l is correct, for 3 marks.

(b) l intersects the x-axis when $y = 0$, which gives $x = 1$. P is $(1, 0)$.

l intersects the y-axis when $x = 0$, which gives $y = 2$. Q is $(0, 2)$.

e These coordinates are correct, for 2 marks.

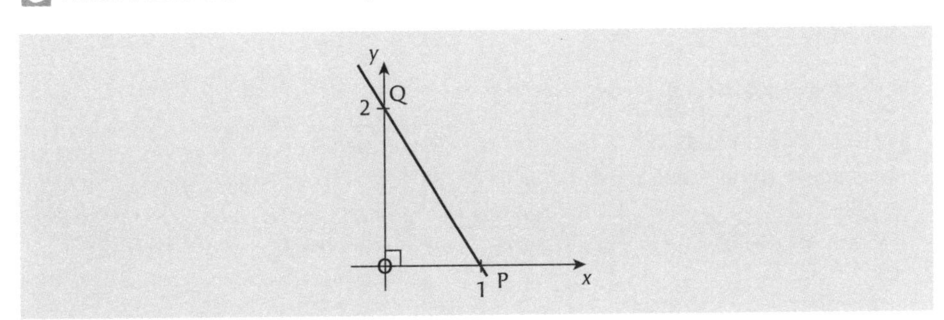

(c) Pythagoras gives PQ $= \sqrt{2^2 + 1^2} = \sqrt{5}$.

e The sketch shows clearly that the length required is the hypotenuse of a right-angled triangle. The value $\sqrt{5}$ is correct. 2 marks are awarded.

Question 2

The points A(0, 6), B(3, 1) and C(6, k) are vertices of a triangle ABC.

Find the gradient of

(a) AB

(b) BC

in terms of the constant k. (2 marks)

(c) Given that angle ABC is a right angle, find the value of k. (3 marks)

Answer to Question 2: candidate A (2 out of 5 marks)

(a) The gradient of AB is $\frac{1-6}{3-0} = -\frac{5}{3}$.

(b) The gradient of BC is $\frac{k-1}{6-3} = \frac{k-1}{3}$.

These are correct, for 2 marks.

(c) $AB = \sqrt{(3-0)^2 \ (1-6)^2} = \sqrt{34}$

$BC = \sqrt{(6-3)^2 + (k-1)^2} = \sqrt{9 + (k-1)^2} = 3 + (k-1) = 2 + k$

$AC = \sqrt{(6-0)^2 + (k-6)^2} = \sqrt{36 + (k-6)^2} = 6 + (k-6) = k$

Using Pythagoras,

$$k^2 = (2+k)^2 + 34$$

$$k^2 = 4 + 4k + k^2 + 34$$

$$4k = -38$$

$$k = -9.5$$

The candidate has failed to note the connection between the first part of the question and the second part, i.e. you should use the first part to help with the second. Following through the candidate's method, there is an error in the apparent simplification of the square root expressions for BC and AC. Note that

$$\sqrt{9 + (k-1)^2} \neq 3 + (k-1) \text{ and } \sqrt{36 + (k-6)^2} \neq 6 + (k-6)$$

These are two common errors which must be avoided. The candidate gains no marks for part **(c)** of the question.

■ ■ ■

Answer to Question 2: candidate B (5 out of 5 marks)

(a) The gradient of AB is $\frac{1-6}{3-0} = -\frac{5}{3}$.

(b) The gradient of BC is $\frac{k-1}{6-3} = \frac{k-1}{3}$.

These are correct, for 2 marks.

(c) AB is perpendicular to BC. Therefore

$$-\frac{5}{3} = -\frac{1}{\left(\frac{k-1}{3}\right)}$$

$$\therefore \quad -\frac{5}{3} = -\frac{3}{k-1}$$

$$\therefore \quad k - 1 = \frac{9}{5}$$

$$\therefore \quad k = \frac{14}{5} = 2.8$$

e This is a good, clear solution, for full marks. Note that is is acceptable to give k as a decimal since it is exact.

Question 3

The diagram shows circle S with equation $x^2 + y^2 - 2x - 6y + 6 = 0$.

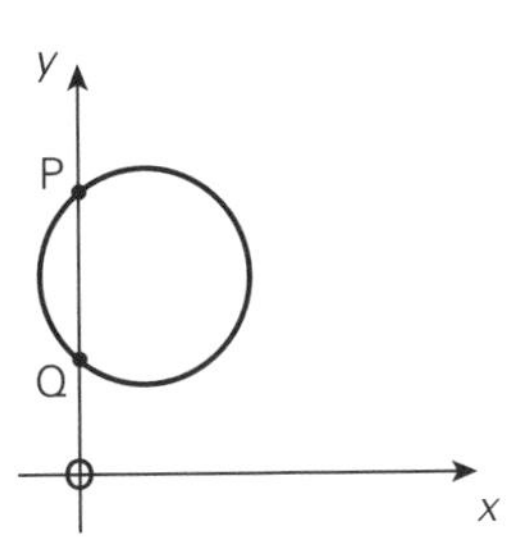

(a) Find
(i) the coordinates of the centre of the circle. (2 marks)
(ii) the radius of S. (2 marks)

(b) The points P and Q are where S intersects the y-axis.
(i) Find the coordinates of P and Q, leaving your answers in the form $a + b\sqrt{c}$. (3 marks)
(ii) Show that the length PQ is $2\sqrt{3}$. (1 mark)
(iii) Find the length of the shortest arc PQ, giving your answer to one decimal place. (3 marks)

Answer to Question 3: candidate A (6 out of 11 marks)

(a) $(x - 1)^2 + (y - 3)^2 - 10 + 6 = 0$

$$(x - 1)^2 + (y - 3)^2 = 4$$

The centre has coordinates $(1, 3)$ and the radius is $\sqrt{4} = 2$.

e This is correct, for 4 marks.

(b) (i) When $x = 0$

$$y^2 - 6y + 6 = 0$$

The formula gives 4.7 and 1.3. P has coordinates (4.7, 0), Q has coordinates (1.3, 0).

e This candidate correctly substitutes $x = 0$ into the equation of the circle to find the y coordinates of P and Q, which gains 1 mark. However, the candidate then gives decimal answers, which are not exact; the question states that answers should be left in surd form, i.e. exact.

(ii) $4.7 - 1.3 = 3.4$

$2\sqrt{3} = 3.464$

e No marks are awarded here since non-exact results have been used.

(iii) The arc length is

$$\frac{90°}{360°} \times 2\pi(2) = 3.14$$

e The candidate has assumed that the angle subtended by the arc is 90°, which is not correct. However, the correct formula has been used together with the correct radius, which gains 1 mark.

Answer to Question 3: candidate B (10 out of 11 marks)

(a) The equation of the circle can be written as

$$(x - 1)^2 - 1 + (y - 3)^2 - 9 + 6 = 0$$

$$(x - 1)^2 + (y - 3)^2 = 4$$

The centre has coordinates (1, 3) and the radius is $\sqrt{4} = 2$.

e This is correct, for full marks.

(b) (i) When $x = 0$

$$1 + (y - 3)^2 = 4$$

$$y^2 - 6y + 6 = 0$$

Solving gives

$$y = \frac{-(-6) \pm \sqrt{36 - 4(6)}}{2}$$

$$= \frac{6 \pm \sqrt{12}}{2}$$

e This is correct, but the y values given are not expressed in the form $a + b\sqrt{c}$, as requested. The candidate should have simplified the expression as follows:

$$\frac{6 \pm \sqrt{12}}{2} = \frac{6}{2} \pm \frac{2\sqrt{3}}{2}$$
$$= 3 \pm \sqrt{3}$$

Also, the solution is longer than it needs to be. When $x = 0$ is substituted to find the y values, a simpler approach would be

$$1 + (y - 3)^2 = 4$$

i.e. $(y - 3)^2 = 3$

$\therefore$ $y - 3 = \pm\sqrt{3}$

$\therefore$ $y = 3 \pm \sqrt{3}$

Thus, P has coordinates $(0, 3 + \sqrt{3})$ and Q has coordinates $(0, 3 - \sqrt{3})$. The candidate's answer gains 2 marks out of 3.

(ii) The distance PQ is the difference in y values,

$$PQ = \frac{6 + \sqrt{12}}{2} - \frac{6 - \sqrt{12}}{2}$$
$$= \sqrt{12} = 2\sqrt{3}$$

This is correct and explained well, for 1 mark.

(iii) The arc length PQ is $\frac{\alpha}{360°} \times 2\pi r = \frac{\alpha 2\pi\,(2)}{360°} = \frac{\alpha\pi}{90°}$.

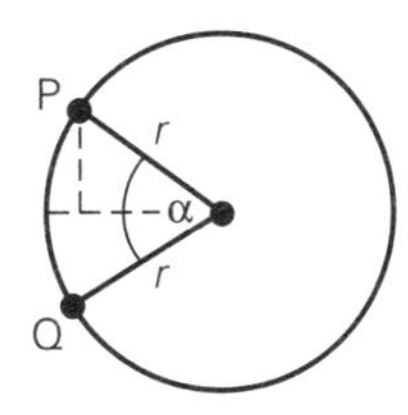

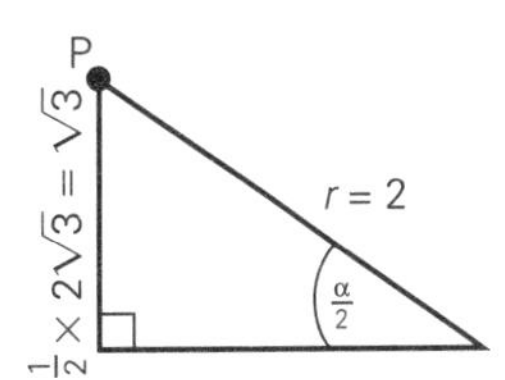

From the triangle,

$$\sin\left(\frac{\alpha}{2}\right) = \frac{\sqrt{3}}{2}$$

$\therefore$ $\frac{\alpha}{2} = 60°$

$\therefore$ $\alpha = 120°$

The arc length is $\frac{120\pi}{90} = 4.2$ (1 d.p.).

This is correct, for 3 marks.

Section 4

Sequences and series

Question 1

The third term of a geometric series is 6 and the seventh is 24. Find the possible values of the common ratio and the first term of the series. (6 marks)

■ ■ ■

Answer to Question 1: candidate A (3 out of 6 marks)

If the third term is 6, this gives $ar^2 = 6$ and so $a = \frac{6}{r^2}$. Substituting into $ar^6 = 24$ gives

$$\frac{6}{r^2}r^6 = 24$$

$$r^4 = 4$$

$$r = 1.4$$

The use of the *n*th term is correct for both the third term and the seventh; this scores 2 marks.

Therefore, $a = \frac{6}{(1.4)^2} = 3.06$

The result $r^4 = 4$ is correct, but the candidate then uses a calculator to find a decimal answer that is non-exact and also misses the negative solution $-\sqrt{2}$. So, just 1 mark is scored out of a possible 3. The answer for *a*, the first term, is incorrect (no marks) because *r* rounded to 1 decimal place is used.

■ ■ ■

Answer to Question 1: candidate B (6 out of 6 marks)

Using the formula for the *n*th term gives

$$ar^2 = 6 \qquad (1)$$

and

$$ar^6 = 24 \qquad (2)$$

Dividing (2) by (1):

$$r^4 = \frac{24}{6} = 4$$

$$\therefore \quad r^2 = 2$$

$\therefore \quad r = \pm\sqrt{2}$

Substituting into (1):

$$a\,(2) = 6, \text{ so } a = 3$$

This is correct and very clear, for full marks. The candidate has labelled the equations and explained what they are doing at each stage of the solution.

Question 2

(a) A child's swing is set swinging. The first swing is through $\alpha°$ and each subsequent swing is $\frac{2}{3}$ of the one before. Write down the angle of the fifth swing. (2 marks)

(b) Given that the total angle through which the swing swings before it comes to rest is 120°, find α. (3 marks)

■ ■ ■

Answer to Question 2: candidate A (0 out of 5 marks)

(a) Fifth swing is $\alpha \times \left(\frac{2}{3}\right)^5 = 0.01024\alpha$

This candidate hasn't recognised that the sequence is $\alpha, \frac{2}{3}\alpha, \left(\frac{2}{3}\right)^2\alpha\ldots$ — a GP. The angle of the 5th swing will be $\alpha\left(\frac{2}{3}\right)^{5-1} = \alpha\left(\frac{2}{3}\right)^4 = \frac{16}{81}\alpha$. The candidate has not attempted the final part of the question and has not recognised this as the sum to infinity of a GP. No marks are awarded.

■ ■ ■

Answer to Question 2: candidate B (5 out of 5 marks)

(a) The angles of swing form a GP: $\alpha, \alpha\left(\frac{2}{3}\right), \alpha\left(\frac{2}{3}\right)^2, \ldots$ so the angle of the 5th swing is

$$\alpha\left(\frac{2}{3}\right)^4 = \frac{16}{81}\alpha°$$

(b) The common ratio of this GP is $\frac{2}{3}$, which is less than 1. Therefore, the sum to infinity exists. This gives

$$S_\infty = \frac{a}{1-r}$$

$$\therefore \quad 120° = \frac{\alpha}{\left(1-\frac{2}{3}\right)}$$

$$\therefore \quad \alpha = 40°$$

This is correct and explained well. It gains full marks.

Question 3

Expand each of the following in ascending powers of x up to and including the term in x^3.

(a) $(1 + 2x)^5$ (3 marks)

(b) $(1 - 3x)^5$ (3 marks)

(c) Deduce the first three terms in the binomial expansion of $(1 - x - 6x^2)^5$. (3 marks)

■ ■ ■

Answer to Question 3: candidate A (3 out of 9 marks)

(a) $(1 + 2x)^5 = 1 + \binom{5}{1}(2x) + \binom{5}{2}(2x)^2 + \binom{5}{3}(2x)^3 + \dots$

$= 1 + 10x + 40x^2 + 80x^3 + \dots$

e This is correct, for 3 marks.

(b) $(1 - 3x)^5 = 1 + \binom{5}{1}(3x) + \binom{5}{2}(3x)^2 + \binom{5}{3}(3x)^3 + \dots$

$= 1 + 15x + 90x^2 + 270x^3 + \dots$

e This candidate has not taken account of the negative coefficient of x and scores no marks. Writing it as $(1 + (-3x))^5$ helps to illustrate what has gone wrong in the solution.

(c) $(1 - x - 6x^2)^5 = (1 - (x + 6x^2))^5 = 1 + \binom{5}{1}(x + 6x^2) + \binom{5}{2}(x + 6x^2)^2 + \dots$

$= 1 + 5(x + 6x^2) + 10(x + 6x^2)^2 + \dots$

e This candidate has not realised that the final part of the question is linked to the first part, i.e. $(1 - x - 6x^2) = (1 + 2x)(1 - 3x)$. However, the method the candidate uses would give the first three terms. Unfortunately, this candidate has ignored the negative sign attached to $(x + 6x^2)$. Also, the answer requires the first three terms in the form $A + Bx + Cx^2$. No marks are awarded.

■ ■ ■

Answer to Question 3: candidate B (9 out of 9 marks)

(a) $(1 + 2x)^5 = 1 + \binom{5}{1}(2x) + \binom{5}{2}(2x)^2 + \binom{5}{3}(2x)^3 + \dots$

$= 1 + 10x + 40x^2 + 80x^3 + \dots$

(b) $(1 - 3x)^5 = 1 + \binom{5}{1}(-3x) + \binom{5}{2}(-3x)^2 + \binom{5}{3}(-3x)^3 + \ldots$

$= 1 - 15x + 90x^2 - 270x^3 + \ldots$

(c) $(1 - x - 6x^2)^5 = ((1 + 2x)(1 - 3x))^5 = (1 + 2x)^5 (1 - 3x)^5$

$= (1 + 10x + 40x^2 + \ldots)(1 - 15x + 90x^2 + \ldots)$

$= 1 - 15x + 90x^2 + 10x - 150x^2 + 40x^2 + \ldots$

$= 1 - 5x - 20x^2 + \ldots$

e This candidate has answered all parts of the question correctly, for 9 marks.

Question 4

The first, second and third terms of a geometric series are p, p^2 and q respectively, where $p < 0$. The first, second and third terms of an arithmetic series are p, q and p^2 respectively.

(a) Find the values of p and q. (6 marks)

(b) Find the sum of the first six terms of the arithmetic series. (3 marks)

Answer to Question 4: candidate A (2 out of 9 marks)

(a) $a = p$, $ar = p^2$, $ar^2 = q$. Substituting gives $pr = p^2$ and $pr^2 = q$.

Therefore, $r = p$ and $p^3 = q$.

$a = p, a + d = q, a + 2d = p^2$

Substituting gives $p + d = q$ and $p + 2d = p^2$.

Therefore, $d = q - p$ and $p + 2(q - p) = p^2$.

e Using the information about the GP, this candidate has correctly derived the relationship $p^3 = q$, for 1 mark, and has derived a correct relationship of $p + 2(q - p) = p^2$, using the information about the AP, for a second mark. However, the candidate has failed to solve these two equations simultaneously for p and q. It is difficult to follow what substitutions are being made, because the candidate doesn't explain fully what he/she is doing.

(b) Sum of first six terms $= p + q + p^2 + (a + 3d) + (a + 4d) + (a + 5d)$

$= p + q + p^2 + 3a + 12d$

e The candidate has not found d, the common difference, and hence cannot simplify. No marks are awarded.

Answer to Question 4: candidate B (7 out of 9 marks)

(a) GP: p, p^2, q, so $r = \dfrac{p^2}{p}$ and $r = \dfrac{q}{p^2}$. Therefore, putting these equal,

$$p = \frac{q}{p^2} \Rightarrow p^3 = q \quad (1)$$

AP: p, q, p^2, so $d = q - p$ and $d = p^2 - q$. Therefore, putting these equal,

$$2q = p^2 + p \qquad (2)$$

Substituting q from (1) into (2),

$$2p^3 = p^2 + p$$

i.e. $\quad 2p^3 - p^2 - p = 0$

i.e. $\quad 2p^2 - p - 1 = 0$

$\therefore \quad (2p + 1)(p - 1) = 0$

$\therefore \quad p = -\frac{1}{2}$ or $p = 1$

If $p = -\frac{1}{2}$ then $q = \left(-\frac{1}{2}\right)^3 = -\frac{1}{8}$. If $p = 1$ then $q = 1$.

e This approach to finding the relationships between p and q is very good and uses the basic properties of GPs and APs, for 2 marks. This candidate derives the correct cubic equation in p, which gains 1 mark, but the division throughout by p to obtain the quadratic $2p^2 - p - 1$ means that a possible solution is lost. The correct approach is:

$$2p^3 - p^2 - p = 0$$

$\therefore \quad p(2p^2 - p - 1) = 0$

$\therefore \quad p(2p + 1)(p - 1) = 0$

$\therefore \quad p = 0$ or $p = -\frac{1}{2}$ or $p = 1$

The candidate then fails to notice that the question states that $p < 0$, which means that only the solution $p = -\frac{1}{2}$ is possible, so marks are lost here. However, 1 mark is gained for calculating the value of q correctly when $p = -\frac{1}{2}$.

(b) For the AP: $d = q - p = -\frac{1}{8} - \left(-\frac{1}{2}\right) = \frac{3}{8}$ or $d = 1 - 1 = 0$.

Using $d = \frac{3}{8}$,

$$S_n = \frac{n}{2}(a + (n - 1)d)$$

$$\therefore \quad S_6 = 3\left(-\frac{1}{2} + 5 \times \frac{3}{8}\right)$$

$$= \frac{33}{8}$$

e The candidate appears to realise that the solution $p = 1$, $q = 1$ gives the trivial case of an AP with no common difference. The solution for the sum of the first six terms is correct, for 3 marks.

Question 5

$$f(x) = \frac{1}{(1+x)^3}, \quad |x| < 1$$

(a) Expand $f(x)$ in ascending powers of x up to and including the term in x^3.

(3 marks)

(b) Hence, show that for small x,

$$f(x) \approx 1 - 3x + 6x^2$$

(1 mark)

(c) Using the polynomial approximation derived in **(b)**, find an approximate value for

$$\int_0^{\frac{1}{4}} \frac{1}{(1+x)^3}\,dx$$

(4 marks)

(d) Explain why it would not be appropriate to estimate the definite integral

$$\int_0^{2} \frac{1}{(1+x)^3}\,dx$$

using the same approximation.

(2 marks)

■ ■ ■

Answer to Question 5: candidate A (7 out of 10 marks)

(a) $f(x) = (1+x)^{-3} = 1 + (-3)x + \frac{(-3)(-3-1)}{2!}x^2 + \frac{(-3)(-3-1)(-3-2)}{3!}x^3 + \ldots$

$$= 1 - 3x + 6x^2 - 10x^3 + \ldots$$

e This is correct, for 3 marks.

(b) Taking the first three terms gives

$$f(x) = 1 - 3x + 6x^2$$

e No marks are gained here as there is no explanation as to why the x^3 term is not needed. The use of the equals sign is also incorrect as $1 - 3x + 6x$ is an approximation for $f(x)$.

(c) $\int_0^{\frac{1}{4}} 1 - 3x + 6x^2\,dx = \left[x - \frac{3x^2}{2} + \frac{6x^3}{3}\right]_0^{\frac{1}{4}}$

$$= \frac{1}{4} - \frac{3}{2}\left(\frac{1}{4}\right)^2 + 2\left(\frac{1}{4}\right)^3 - 0 = \frac{3}{16}$$

The estimate of $\frac{3}{16}$ is correct, for 4 marks.

(d) Because the limit 2 is not a fraction.

The final part is incorrect. To see this, consider $\frac{21}{4}$, which is a fraction, as the upper limit. The method used would still not be appropriate.

■ ■ ■

Answer to Question 5: candidate B (9 out of 10 marks)

(a) $f(x) = (1 + x)^{-3} = 1 + (-3)x + \frac{(-3)(-3-1)}{2!}x^2 + \frac{(-3)(-3-1)(-3-2)}{3!}x^3 + ...$

$= 1 - 3x + 6x^2 - 10x^3 + ...$

This is correct, for 3 marks.

(b) For small x, $x^3 \approx 0$. Therefore,

$f(x) \approx 1 - 3x + 6x^2$

This is correct and written very clearly, for 1 mark.

(c) $\int_0^{\frac{1}{4}} \frac{1}{(1+x)^3}\, dx \approx \int_0^{\frac{1}{4}} 1 - 3x + 6x^2\, dx$

$$= \left[x - \frac{3x^2}{2} + 2x^3\right]_0^{\frac{1}{4}}$$

$$= \frac{1}{4} - \frac{3}{32} + \frac{1}{32} = \frac{3}{16}$$

The estimate of $\frac{3}{16}$ is correct and use of the approximation sign is appropriate. 4 marks are awarded.

(d) It would not be appropriate to estimate

$$\int_0^2 \frac{1}{(1+x)^3}\, dx$$

using the approximation $\frac{1}{(1+x)^3} \approx 1 - 3x + 6x^2$ because the polynomial expansion is only valid for small x such that $|x| < 1$.

This gains 1 mark, but the candidate has not explained clearly that the range $0 \leqslant x \leqslant 2$ covered by the limits goes outside the valid interval. Plus, the polynomial expansion derived in **(b)** is not valid for the entire range $0 \leqslant x \leqslant 1$, since it is only valid for small x.

Trigonometry

Question 1

Solve the equation $\cos(2\theta + 30°) = 0.3$ for $0° < \theta < 180°$, giving your answers to two decimal places. (4 marks)

■ ■ ■

Answer to Question 1: candidate A (2 out of 4 marks)

$$\cos(2\theta + 30°) = 0.3$$

$$\therefore \quad 2\theta + 30° = 72.54°$$

$$\therefore \quad \theta = 21.27°$$

This candidate has correctly found one solution, for 2 marks, but has not changed the range to match $(2\theta + 30°)$. This means that the other possible solution has not been found.

■ ■ ■

Answer to Question 1: candidate B (4 out of 4 marks)

If $0 < \theta < 180°$, then $30° < 2\theta + 30° < 390°$ becomes the new range.

$$\cos(2\theta + 30°) = 0.3$$

$$\therefore \quad 2\theta + 30° = 72.54° \text{ or } 287.46°$$

$$\therefore \quad \theta = 21.27° \text{ or } 128.73°$$

This candidate has changed the range and successfully found the two possible solutions. (4 marks)

Question 2

Find, in degrees, the values of θ in the interval $0° \leqslant \theta \leqslant 360°$ for which

$$2\sin^2\theta = \cos\theta + 2$$

(5 marks)

■ ■ ■

Answer to Question 2: candidate A (0 out of 5 marks)

$\cos\theta = 1 - \sin\theta$; substituting gives

$$2\sin^2\theta = 1 - \sin\theta + 2$$

$$2\sin^2\theta + \sin\theta - 3 = 0$$

$$(2\sin\theta + 3)(\sin\theta - 1) = 0$$

$$\sin\theta = -\frac{3}{2} \text{ or } \sin\theta = 1$$

$$\theta = 90°$$

e This candidate gains no marks at all for this 'neat' solution. The original substitution is incorrect as $\cos\theta \neq 1 - \sin\theta$. The candidate has used the true identity $\cos^2\theta = 1 - \sin^2\theta$ and then appears to have taken the square root of both sides and concluded, incorrectly, that $\sqrt{1 - \sin^2\theta} = 1 - \sin\theta$ — a common mistake.

■ ■ ■

Answer to Question 2: candidate B (5 out of 5 marks)

Using $\sin^2\theta = 1 - \cos^2\theta$ gives

$$2(1 - \cos^2\theta) = \cos\theta + 2$$

$\therefore \quad 2 - 2\cos^2\theta - \cos\theta - 2 = 0$

$\therefore \quad -2\cos^2\theta - \cos\theta = 0$

$\therefore \quad -\cos\theta(2\cos\theta + 1) = 0$

$\therefore \quad \cos\theta = 0 \text{ or } \cos\theta = -\frac{1}{2}$

$\cos\theta = 0$ gives $\theta = 90°, 270°$

$\cos\theta = -\frac{1}{2}$ gives $\theta = 120°, 240°$

e This is correct, for 5 marks.

Question 3

(a) Show that $\sin 2\theta - 2\cos 2\theta = 0$ can be written in the form $\tan 2\theta = 2$. (2 marks)

(b) Hence, solve the equation $\sin 2\theta - 2\cos 2\theta = 0$ for $0° \leqslant \theta \leqslant 180°$, giving your answers to one decimal place. (3 marks)

■ ■ ■

Answer to Question 3: candidate A (2 out of 5 marks)

(a) $\sin 2\theta \ = 2\cos 2\theta$

Divide by 2:

$$\sin\theta = \cos\theta$$

$$\therefore \quad \frac{\sin\theta}{\cos\theta} = 1$$

$\therefore \quad \tan\theta = 1$, which is the same as $\tan 2\theta = 2$.

e It seems that this candidate cannot deal with the multiple angles, 2θ, and attempts to transform them into something more familiar by dividing by 2. This is incorrect and scores no marks.

(b) $\tan 2\theta = 2$

$$2\theta = 63.4° \text{ or } 243.4°$$

$$\theta = 31.7° \text{ as } 243.4° \text{ is out of range}$$

e The two possible answers for 2θ are correct, for 2 marks, but the mark for the final answers is lost because 243.4 is not outside the range for 2θ.

■ ■ ■

Answer to Question 3: candidate B (5 out of 5 marks)

(a) Divide throughout by $\cos 2\theta$:

$$\frac{\sin 2\theta}{\cos 2\theta} - 2\frac{\cos 2\theta}{\cos 2\theta} = 0$$

$$\therefore \quad \tan 2\theta = 2$$

e This is correct, for 2 marks.

(b) Change the range from $0 \leqslant \theta \leqslant 180°$ to $0 \leqslant 2\theta \leqslant 360°$:

$$\tan 2\theta = 2$$

$$\therefore \quad 2\theta = 63.4° \text{ or } 243.4°$$

$$\therefore \quad \theta = 31.7° \text{ or } 121.7°$$

e This is correct, for 3 marks. Notice that this candidate changes the range at the start of the solution to avoid missing possible solutions.

Question 4

The angle α is acute and $\sin\alpha = \frac{1}{\sqrt{5}}$. Show that

(a) $\sin\alpha + \cos\alpha = \frac{3}{\sqrt{5}}$ (3 marks)

(b) $\tan\alpha = \frac{1}{2}$ (2 marks)

■ ■ ■

Answer to Question 4: candidate A (0 out of 5 marks)

(a)

$$\sin\alpha = 0.447$$

$$\therefore \quad \alpha = 26.565°$$

$$\therefore \quad \cos\alpha = 0.894$$

$$\therefore \quad \sin\alpha + \cos\alpha = 0.447 + 0.894 = 1.341$$

Now, $\frac{3}{\sqrt{5}} = 1.341$, which is the same.

ⓔ This candidate has not realised from the question that exact answers are to be used throughout. All the decimals used are rounded (in some cases incorrectly) and approximations are used. This attempt gains no marks.

(b) If $\alpha = 26.565°$ then $\tan\alpha = 0.49999$, which is the same as 0.5.

ⓔ Again, non-exact methods are used, so no marks are awarded.

■ ■ ■

Answer to Question 4: candidate B (2 out of 5 marks)

(a) If $\sin\alpha = \frac{1}{\sqrt{5}}$, use $\cos^2\alpha + \sin^2\alpha = 1$:

$$\cos^2\alpha = 1 + \left(\frac{1}{\sqrt{5}}\right)^2$$

$$= 1 + \frac{1}{5} = \frac{6}{5}$$

$$\cos\alpha = \sqrt{\frac{6}{5}}$$

Therefore, $\sin\alpha + \cos\alpha = \frac{1}{\sqrt{5}} + \frac{\sqrt{6}}{\sqrt{5}} = \frac{1+\sqrt{6}}{\sqrt{5}}$.

ⓔ This method of using $\cos^2\alpha + \sin^2\alpha = 1$ is correct and gains 1 mark. The candidate then makes a careless error with signs ($\cos^2\alpha = 1 - \left(\frac{1}{\sqrt{5}}\right)^2$ is correct) which results in the answer $\cos\alpha = \sqrt{\frac{6}{5}}$. At this point, the candidate should have noticed that $\sqrt{\frac{6}{5}}$ is greater than 1, which is not possible for $\cos\alpha$.

(b) Now, $\tan\alpha = \dfrac{\sin\alpha}{\cos\alpha} = \dfrac{\left(\frac{1}{\sqrt{5}}\right)}{\left(\frac{\sqrt{6}}{\sqrt{5}}\right)} = \dfrac{1}{\sqrt{6}}$

e This answer is incorrect, because the candidate uses the wrong values from part **(a)**. However, the method is correct and gains 1 mark.

Question 5

Express $3\sin x + \cos x$ in the form $R\sin(x + \alpha)$, where $R > 0$ and $0 \leqslant \alpha \leqslant \frac{\pi}{2}$.
(4 marks)

(a) State the maximum value of $f(x) = 10 + 3\sin x + \cos x$ and the value of x for which this maximum occurs. (3 marks)

(b) The graph of $y = 3\sin x + \cos x$ may be obtained from the graph of $y = \sin x$ by means of two successive transformations. Describe these transformations and sketch the graph of $y = 3\sin x + \cos x$ for $0 \leqslant x \leqslant 360°$. (4 marks)

■ ■ ■

Answer to Question 5: candidate A (1 out of 11 marks)

$$R\sin(x + \alpha) = R\sin x\cos\alpha + \cos x\sin\alpha = 3\sin x + \cos x$$

So, $R\sin x\cos\alpha = 3\sin x$, which gives $R\cos\alpha = 3$.

Also, $\cos x\sin\alpha = \cos x$, which gives $\sin\alpha = 0$.

Therefore, $\alpha = 0$ and $R = 3$.

e Although this candidate has written down the correct expansion for $\sin(x + \alpha)$, the R term has been missed out for the term $\cos x\sin\alpha$. The candidate has then correctly compared two of the terms and derived the relationship $R\cos\alpha = 3$, which gains 1 mark. However, the second comparison is incorrect due to the missing R term.

(a) The maximum value of $f(x)$ is 13 when x is 90°.

e This is incorrect. Candidate A has not realised that there is a connection between the first part, $R\sin(x + \alpha)$, and this part of the question.

(b) Multiply by 3 and add $\cos x$.

e The mistake here is thinking that 'adding $\cos x$' is a translation. This is incorrect.

■ ■ ■

Answer to Question 5: candidate B (9 out of 11 marks)

$$R\sin(x + \alpha) = R\sin x\cos\alpha + R\cos x\sin\alpha$$

Comparing with $3\sin x + \cos x$ gives

$$R\cos\alpha = 3 \text{ and } R\sin\alpha = 1$$

Therefore, $\tan\alpha = \frac{1}{3}$, giving $\alpha = 18.4°$.

Also, $R^2 = 1^2 + 3^2 = 10$. Therefore, $R = \sqrt{10}$.

This gives

$$3\sin x + \cos x = \sqrt{10}\sin(x + 18.4°)$$

e The first part is correct, for 4 marks.

(a) $f(x) = 10 + \sqrt{10}\sin(x + 18.4°)$. The maximum value of $\sin(x + 18.4°)$ is 1, which occurs when $x + 18.4° = 90°$, i.e. $x = 71.6°$. Therefore, the maximum value of $f(x)$ is $10 + \sqrt{10}$.

e This is correct, for 3 marks.

(b) A translation of 18.4 in the negative x-direction, followed by a stretch.

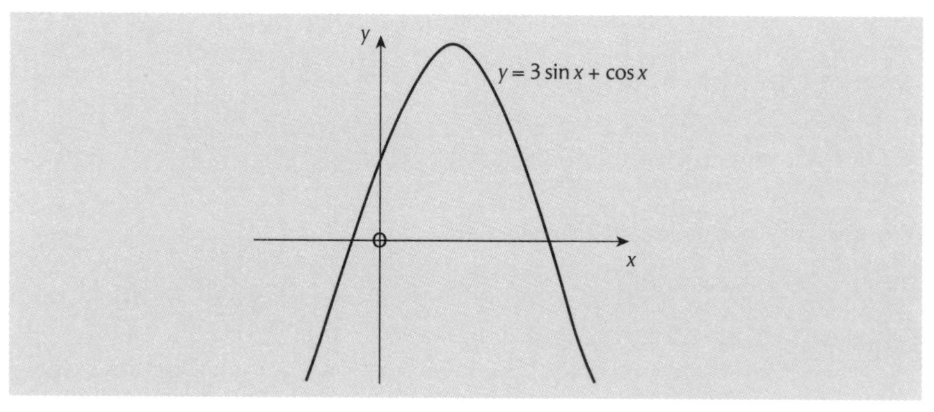

e The translation description is correct, which gains 1 mark. Although there is a stretch, this candidate does not give a full description. It is a stretch parallel to the y axis by a scale factor of $\sqrt{10}$. The sketch graph is correct, for 1 mark.

Question 6

Solve the equation $1 + \tan x = 2\cot x$, for $0° \leqslant x \leqslant 360°$. (6 marks)

■ ■ ■

Answer to Question 6: candidate A (3 out of 6 marks)

Using $\cot x = \dfrac{1}{\tan x}$, the equation becomes $1 + \tan x = 2\dfrac{1}{\tan x}$.

Trying values gives $\tan x = 1$.

Therefore, $x = 45°$ and $225°$.

This candidate has made the correct substitution. However, using trial and error this candidate has only found one of the possible solutions for $\tan x$. The candidate gains 1 mark for the substitution $\cot x = \frac{1}{\tan x}$, 1 mark for $\tan x = 1$ and 1 mark for the x solutions.

■ ■ ■

Answer to Question 6: candidate B (5 out of 6 marks)

$$1 + \tan x = \frac{2}{\tan x}$$

$$\therefore \quad \tan x + \tan^2 x = 2$$

$$\therefore \quad \tan^2 x + \tan x - 2 = 0$$

$$\therefore \quad (\tan x - 1)(\tan x + 2) = 0$$

$$\therefore \quad \tan x = 1 \text{ or } \tan x = -2$$

If $\tan x = 1$ then $x = 45°$, and $180° + 45° = 225°$.

If $\tan x = -2$ then $x = -63.4°$, and $-180° - 63.4° = -243.4°$.

All 4 marks are gained for the solution through to the results $\tan x = 1$ and $\tan x = -2$. The solutions for x corresponding to $\tan x = 1$ are correct, which gains 1 mark. The solutions corresponding to $\tan x = -2$ are outside the range $0° \leqslant x \leqslant 360°$, which loses the final mark. The correct solutions are 116.6° and 296.6°.

Question 7

Using the approximations $\sin x \approx x$ and $\cos x \approx 1 - \frac{1}{2}x^2$, solve the equation

$3\sin x + 2\cos x = 2.12$

where x is small and measured in radians. (4 marks)

■ ■ ■

Answer to Question 7: candidate A (1 out of 4 marks)

$$3x + 2\left(1 - \frac{1}{2}x^2\right) = 2.12$$

$$\therefore \quad 3x + 2 - \frac{1}{2}x^2 = 2.12$$

$$\therefore \quad -\frac{1}{2}x^2 + 3x - 0.12 = 0$$

$$\therefore \quad -x^2 + 6x - 0.24 = 0$$

Therefore, $x = \dfrac{-6 \pm \sqrt{36 - 4(1)(-0.24)}}{2} = 0.04$ or -6.04.

The substitutions are correct, for 1 mark. However, the expansion of the bracket in the first line of working is wrong, giving an incorrect quadratic equation in x. A second mistake is then made in the quadratic formula: the coefficient of x^2 is -1 and not 1, as used by the candidate in the formula.

■ ■ ■

Answer to Question 7: candidate B (3 out of 4 marks)

$$3x + 2\left(1 - \frac{1}{2}x^2\right) = 2.12$$

$$\therefore \quad 3x + 2 - x^2 = 2.12$$

$$\therefore \quad x^2 - 3x + 0.12 = 0$$

The quadratic formula gives $x = 2.959$ and 0.041.

This is correct, except that the candidate should have eliminated the solution 2.959 on the grounds that it is too large (the question states that x is small). A quick check by substituting $x = 2.959$ into the original equation shows that it is not a valid solution. 3 marks are awarded.

Question 8

(a) Use the identities for $\sin(A + B)$ and $\cos(A + B)$ to show
  (i) $\sin 2A = 2\sin A\cos A$ (1 mark)
  (ii) $\cos 2A = \cos^2 A - \sin^2 A$ (1 mark)

(b) Hence, prove that $\sin 3A = 3\sin A - 4\sin^3 A$. (5 marks)

(c) Solve the equation $\sin 3\theta - 2\sin\theta = 0$ for $0° \leqslant \theta \leqslant 360°$. (8 marks)

■ ■ ■

Answer to Question 8: candidate A (6 out of 15 marks)

(a) (i) $\sin(A + B) = \sin A\cos B + \cos A\sin B$.

Let $B = A$, therefore $\sin 2A = 2\sin A\cos A$

This is correct, for 1 mark.

(ii) $\cos(A + B) = \cos A\cos B - \sin A\sin B$

Let $B = A$, therefore $\cos 2A = \cos^2 A - \sin^2 A$

This is correct, for 1 mark.

(b) $\sin 3A = 3\sin A - 4\sin^3 A$

This candidate has left out the identity proof part of the question (worth 5 marks).

(c)

$$3\sin\theta - 4\sin^3\theta - 2\sin\theta = 0$$

$$\therefore \quad \sin\theta - 4\sin^3\theta = 0$$

$$\therefore \quad 1 - 4\sin^2\theta = 0$$

$$\therefore \quad \sin^2\theta = \frac{1}{4}$$

$$\therefore \quad \sin\theta = \frac{1}{2}$$

$$\therefore \quad \theta = 30°, 150°$$

Although the candidate did not prove the identity (part **(b)**), he/she has realised that the identity for $\sin 3A$ is required to answer **(c)**, and used the given identity. This is a good technique. The substitution and simplification are correct and gain 2 marks. However, this candidate has divided throughout by $\sin\theta$ (line 2 to line 3), rather than take out a factor of $\sin\theta$. This has resulted in the loss of a possible solution, $\sin\theta = 0$. Although $\sin^2\theta = \frac{1}{4}$ is correct, this gives rise to two possible solutions: $\sin\theta = +\frac{1}{2}$ and $\sin\theta = -\frac{1}{2}$; one of these is missing. However, 2 marks are awarded for $\sin\theta = \frac{1}{2}$ and two correct values for θ, giving a total of 4 marks for **(c)**.

■ ■ ■

Answer to Question 8: candidate A (15 out of 15 marks)

(a) (i) $\sin(A + B) = \sin A\cos B + \cos A\sin B$

Let $B = A$, giving $\sin(A + A) = \sin A\cos A + \sin A\cos A$.

Therefore, $\sin 2A = 2\sin A\cos A$.

This is correct, for 1 mark.

(ii) $\cos(A + B) = \cos A \cos B - \sin A \sin B$.

Let $B = A$, giving $\cos(A + A) = \cos A \cos A - \sin A \sin A$.

Therefore, $\cos 2A = \cos^2 A - \sin^2 A$.

e This is correct, for 1 mark.

(b) $\sin 3A = \sin(2A + A) = \sin 2A \cos A + \cos 2A \sin A$

$$= 2\sin A \cos A \cos A + \sin A(\cos^2 A - \sin^2 A)$$

$$= 2\sin A \cos^2 A + \sin A \cos^2 A - \sin^3 A$$

$$= 3\sin A \cos^2 A - \sin^3 A$$

$$= 3\sin A\,(1 - \sin^2 A) - \sin^3 A$$

$$= 3\sin A - 3\sin^3 A - \sin^3 A$$

$$= 3\sin A - 4\sin^3 A$$

e The identity proof is correct and very clear, for 5 marks.

(c)

$$3\sin\theta - 4\sin^3\theta - 2\sin\theta = 0$$

$$\therefore \quad -4\sin^3\theta + \sin\theta = 0$$

$$\therefore \quad \sin\theta(4\sin^2\theta - 1) = 0$$

$$\therefore \quad \sin\theta = 0 \text{ or } \sin^2\theta = \tfrac{1}{4}$$

If $\sin\theta = 0$, then $\theta = 0, 180°, 360°$.

If $\sin^2\theta = \frac{1}{4}$, then $\sin\theta = \pm\frac{1}{2}$.

If $\sin\theta = \frac{1}{2}$, then $\theta = 30°, 150°$.

If $\sin\theta = -\frac{1}{2}$, then $\theta = -30°, -150°$. In the range $0° \leqslant \theta \leqslant 360°$, $\theta = 210°, 330°$.

e This is a good solution, for full marks.

Exponentials and logarithms

Question 1

Given that p and q are positive constants, simplify fully each of the following:

(a) $\ln\left(\frac{p}{q}\right) + \ln(pq)$ (3 marks)

(b) $e^{2\ln p} - \ln(e^{2q})$ (3 marks)

■ ■ ■

Answer to Question 1: candidate A (2 out of 6 marks)

(a) $\ln\left(\frac{p}{q}\right) + \ln(pq) = \frac{\ln p}{\ln q} + \ln p + \ln q$

$= \ln p - \ln q + \ln p + \ln q$

$= 2\ln p$

e An incorrect rule has been used: $\ln\left(\frac{p}{q}\right) \neq \frac{\ln p}{\ln q}$. If this candidate had not written the incorrect intermediate step $\left(\frac{\ln p}{\ln q}\right)$, this would have qualified for 1 mark, since line 2 of the candidate's solution is correct. The manipulation of $\ln(pq)$ is correct, for 1 mark.

(b) $e^{2\ln p} - \ln(e^{2q}) = 2p - 2q$

e The simplification of the first term is incorrect, so no marks are awarded. The second term is simplified correctly, for 1 mark.

■ ■ ■

Answer to Question 1: candidate B (6 out of 6 marks)

(a) $\ln\left(\frac{p}{q}\right) + \ln(pq) = \ln p - \ln q + \ln p + \ln q$

$= 2\ln p$

e This is correct, for 3 marks. (Notice that this final answer is the same as candidate A's, but candidate A derived it incorrectly.)

(b) $e^{2\ln p} - \ln(e^{2q}) = e^{\ln p^2} - 2q$

$= p^2 - 2q$

e This is correct, for 3 marks.

Question 2

Solve $3^k = 4e^k$, where k is a positive integer, leaving your answer in an exact form.

(5 marks)

■ ■ ■

Answer to Question 2: candidate A (2 out of 5 marks)

$$3^k = 4e^k$$

$$\therefore \quad \ln 3^k = \ln 4e^k$$

$$\therefore \quad k\ln 3 = k\ln 4e$$

$$\therefore \quad \ln 3 = \ln 4e$$

e This candidate has realised that taking logs of both sides is an appropriate method to solve for k. However, $\ln 4e^k \neq k\ln 4e$, since the 4 is not raised to the power k. 1 mark is gained for the method and 1 mark for writing $\ln 3^k = k\ln 3$.

■ ■ ■

Answer to Question 2: candidate B (5 out of 5 marks)

$$3^k = 4e^k$$

$$\therefore \quad \ln 3^k = \ln 4e^k$$

$$\therefore \quad k\ln 3 = \ln 4 + \ln e^k$$

$$\therefore \quad k\ln 3 = \ln 4 + k$$

$$\therefore \quad k(\ln 3 - 1) = \ln 4$$

$$\therefore \quad k = \frac{\ln 4}{\ln 3 - 1}$$

e This is correct and a clear solution, for full marks. Notice that this candidate has left the final answer in an exact form, as required.

Question 3

The function f is given by $f(x) = \ln(4x + 1)$, where x is real and $x > -\frac{1}{4}$.

(a) Find an expression for $f^{-1}(x)$. State the range of f^{-1}. (4 marks)

(b) Sketch the graph of $y = f^{-1}(x)$. (2 marks)

Answer to Question 3: candidate A (2 out of 6 marks)

(a) $f^{-1}(x) = e^{4x+1}$. The range is $x > -\frac{1}{4}$.

The inverse function is incorrect. Although e^x is the inverse of $\ln x$, this does not imply that e^{mx+c} is the inverse of $\ln(mx + c)$. The range is actually $f(x) > -\frac{1}{4}$. No marks are awarded.

(b)

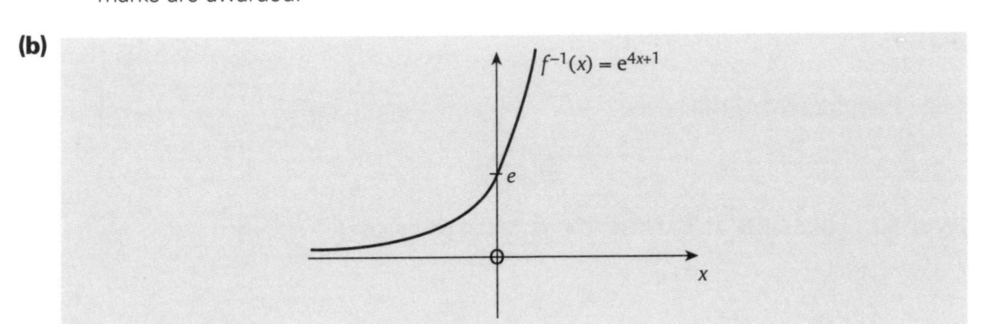

The sketch graph is correct for the inverse function given by the candidate, so 2 marks are awarded in this case. It is worth noting that full marks for the sketch of an incorrect function may not always be awarded.

■ ■ ■

Answer to Question 3: candidate B (5 out of 6 marks)

(a) If $y = \ln(4x + 1)$ then

$$e^y = 4x + 1$$

$$\therefore \quad 4x = e^y - 1$$

$$\therefore \quad x = \frac{e^y - 1}{4}$$

Therefore, $f^{-1}(x) = \dfrac{e^x - 1}{4}$.

The range of f^{-1} is the same as the domain of f. The range is $f(x) > -\frac{1}{4}$.

The first part is correct, for 4 marks.

(b)

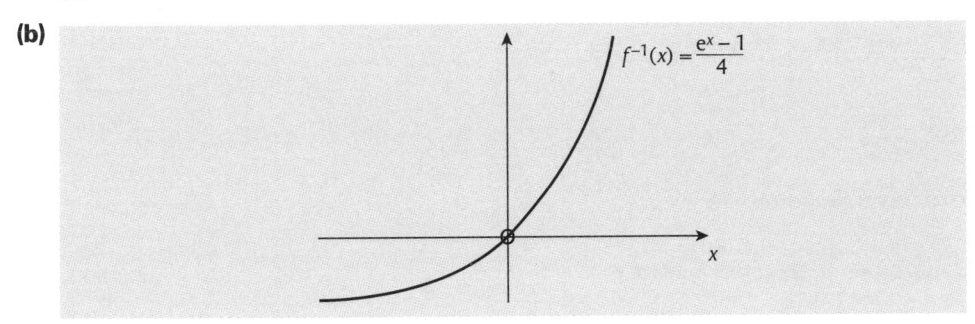

The sketch graph does not show the horizontal asymptote at $-\frac{1}{4}$, which loses 1 mark.

Differentiation

Question 1

Calculate the gradient of the curve $y = x^2 - \dfrac{1}{x}$ at the point $x = \frac{1}{2}$. (4 marks)

■ ■ ■

Answer to Question 1: candidate A (3 out of 4 marks)

$$y = x^2 - x^{-1}$$

$$\therefore \quad \frac{dy}{dx} = 2x + x^0 = 2x$$

$$\text{At } x = \tfrac{1}{2},\ \frac{dy}{dx} = 2 \times \tfrac{1}{2} = 1.$$

e The candidate expresses y in an appropriate form. The differential of x^2 is correct, for 1 mark, but the differential of $-x^{-1}$ is x^{-2}. 1 mark is awarded for the substitution of $x = \frac{1}{2}$ and 1 mark for the evaluation, which is correct for the gradient function derived by the candidate.

■ ■ ■

Answer to Question 1: candidate B (4 out of 4 marks)

$$y = x^2 - x^{-1}$$

$$\therefore \quad \frac{dy}{dx} = 2x + x^{-2}$$

$$\text{At } x = \tfrac{1}{2},\ \frac{dy}{dx} = 2\left(\tfrac{1}{2}\right) + \frac{1}{\left(\tfrac{1}{2}\right)^2} = 5.$$

e This is correct, for 4 marks.

Question 2

A curve has equation $y = e^{2x} - x$.

(a) Determine $\dfrac{dy}{dx}$ as a function of x. (2 marks)

(b) The curve has a single turning point T. Find the coordinates of the turning point T, leaving your answers in exact form. (4 marks)

(c) By considering the gradient of the curve either side of T, determine its nature.
(3 marks)

Answer to Question 2: candidate A (3 out of 9 marks)

(a) $y = e^{2x} - x$

$\therefore \quad \dfrac{dy}{dx} = e^{2x} - 1$

The gradient function is correct, for 2 marks.

(b) At T,

$$\frac{dy}{dx} = 0$$

$\therefore \quad 2e^{2x} - 1 = 0$

This candidate knows that the turning point occurs when the gradient is 0, so 1 mark is awarded. However, the candidate has not been able to solve for x.

(c)

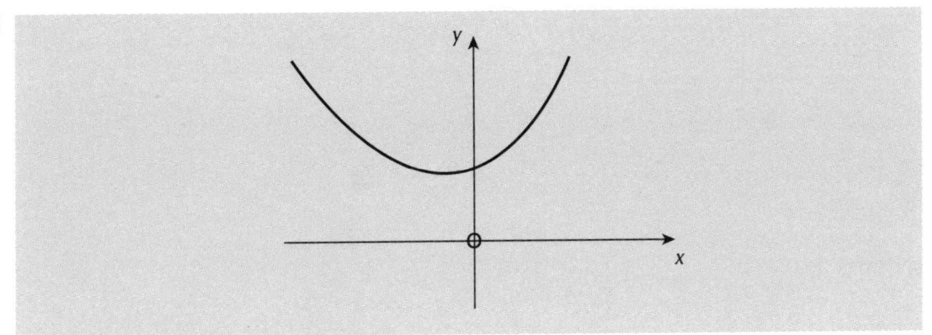

The turning point is a minimum.

Recognising that he/she has been unable to find the required coordinates, this candidate has sketched the graph (correctly) to determine the nature of T. This gains no marks because the question states very specifically that the nature of the curve should be determined by considering the gradient either side of T and not by inspection of the graph.

Answer to Question 2: candidate B (8 out of 9 marks)

(a) $y = e^{2x} - x$

$\therefore \quad \dfrac{dy}{dx} = 2e^{2x} - 1$

This candidate has correctly found the gradient function, for 2 marks.

(b) At a turning point, $\frac{dy}{dx} = 0$, therefore

$$2e^{2x} - 1 = 0$$

$$\therefore \quad e^{2x} = \tfrac{1}{2}$$

$$\therefore \quad \ln e^{2x} = \ln\left(\tfrac{1}{2}\right)$$

$$\therefore \quad 2x\ln e = \ln\left(\tfrac{1}{2}\right)$$

$$\therefore \quad x = \tfrac{1}{2}\ln\left(\tfrac{1}{2}\right)$$

The candidate has solved correctly for x, the x-coordinate of T, for 3 marks. However, he/she has not then substituted back to find the y-coordinate of T (the question asks for the *coordinates*).

(c)

x	-0.5	$\frac{1}{2}\ln\frac{1}{2}$	0
$\frac{dy}{dx}$	-0.264	0	$+1$

The gradients either side of the turning point show that T is a minimum.

This is correct, for 3 marks.

Question 3

Lemonade cans are to be manufactured with base radius of r cm and height h cm.

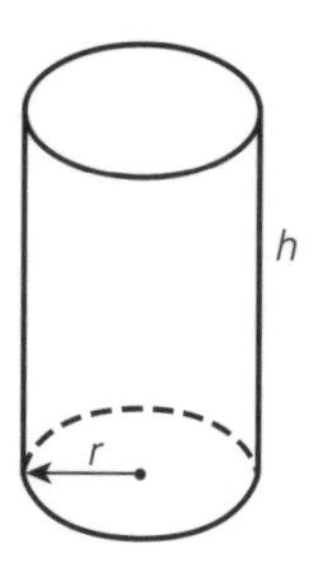

(a) Given that the capacity of a can is to be 600 cm^3,

(i) show that $h = \dfrac{600}{\pi r^2}$ (1 mark)

(ii) show that the surface area, $S\text{cm}^2$, of a can is given by

$$S = \frac{1200}{r} + 2\pi r^2$$ (3 marks)

(b) The surface area needs to be minimised.

(i) By considering $\frac{dS}{dr}$, find the value of r for which S is a minimum. (4 marks)

(ii) Calculate the minimum value of S. (1 mark)

(iii) Verify that this is indeed the minimum value of S. (3 marks)

■ ■ ■

Answer to Question 3: candidate A (3 out of 12 marks)

(a) (i)

$$V = \pi r^2 h$$

$$\pi r^2 h = 600$$

$$\therefore \quad h = \frac{600}{\pi r^2}$$

e This is correct, for 1 mark.

(ii) $S = \pi r^2 + \pi r^2 + rh$

$$= 2\pi r^2 + rh$$

$$= 2\pi r^2 + r\left(\frac{600}{\pi r^2}\right)$$

$$= 2\pi r^2 + \frac{600}{\pi r}$$

e The formula for S is incorrect. However, the substitution for h is the correct method, and is awarded 1 mark.

(b) (i) $\frac{dS}{dr} = 4r + \frac{600}{\pi}$

$$0 = 4r + \frac{600}{\pi}$$

$$4r = -\frac{600}{\pi}, \text{ so } r = -\frac{600}{4\pi}$$

e $\frac{dS}{dr}$ is incorrect. The candidate should have written $S = 2\pi r^2 + \frac{600}{\pi}r^{-1}$ and then differentiated to give $\frac{dS}{dr} = 4\pi r - \frac{600}{\pi}r^{-2}$. 1 mark is gained for putting $\frac{dS}{dr}$ equal to zero. The candidate seems to have realised that the negative value for r is incorrect and therefore not completed the question.

■ ■ ■

Answer to Question 3: candidate B (12 out of 12 marks)

(a) (i) Volume is given by

$$V = \pi r^2 h$$

$$600 = \pi r^2 h$$

$$\therefore \quad h = \frac{600}{\pi r^2}$$

e This is correct, for 1 mark.

(ii) $S = 2\pi r^2 + 2\pi rh$

$$= 2\pi r^2 + 2\pi r\left(\frac{600}{\pi r^2}\right)$$

$$= 2\pi r^2 + \frac{1200}{r}$$

e The formula has been derived correctly, for full marks.

(b) (i) $S = 2\pi r^2 + 1200r^{-1}$

$$\therefore \quad \frac{dS}{dr} = 4\pi r - 1200r^{-2}$$

For a minimum,

$$4\pi r - 1200r^{-2} = 0$$

$$\therefore \quad 4\pi r = \frac{1200}{r^2}$$

$$\therefore \quad r^3 = \frac{1200}{4\pi}$$

$$\therefore \quad r = 4.6 \text{ to 1 decimal place}$$

e The value of r for which S is a minimum is correct, for 4 marks.

(ii) $S = \frac{1200}{4.6} + 2\pi(4.6)^2 = 393.8.$

e This is correct, for 1 mark.

(iii)

r	4	4.6	5
$\frac{dS}{dr}$	−24.7	0	+14.8

The signs of the gradients either side show that S is a minimum.

e The candidate has verified correctly that the value for S is a minimum and is awarded full marks.

Question 4

Given that $f(x) = x + \frac{1}{x^2}, x \neq 0$,

(a) determine $f'(x)$ (2 marks)

(b) determine the intervals for which f is an increasing function (3 marks)

■ ■ ■

Answer to Question 4: candidate A (3 out of 5 marks)

(a) $f(x) = x + x^{-2}$

$\therefore \quad f'(x) = 1 - 2x^{-3}$

e This is correct, for 2 marks.

(b) (see graph)

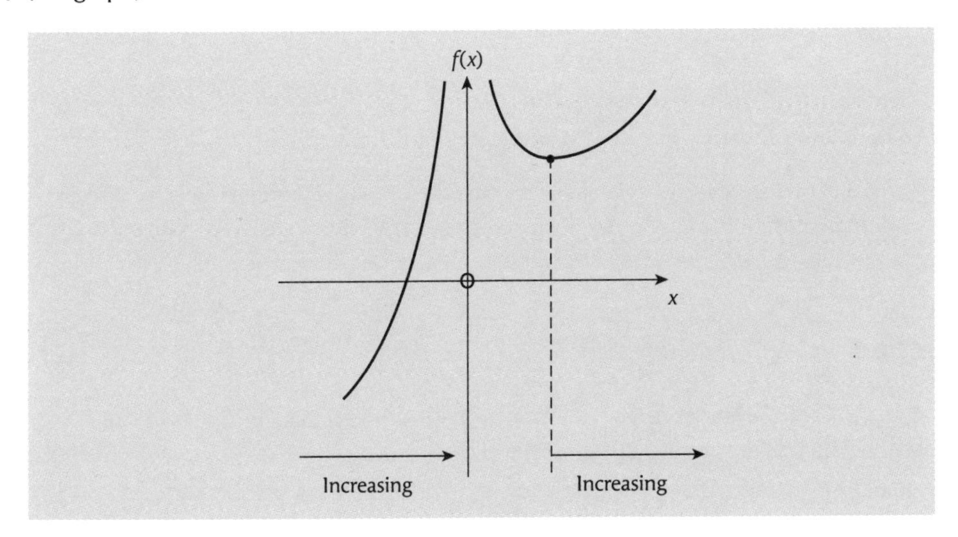

e Although the graph is correct and the increasing sections identified, for 1 mark, the intervals are not given in the required detail, for example $x < 0$.

■ ■ ■

Answer to Question 4: candidate B (4 out of 5 marks)

(a) $f(x) = x + x^{-2}$

$\therefore \quad f'(x) = 1 - 2x^{-3} = 1 - \frac{2}{x^3}$

e This is correct, for 2 marks. Notice that although not required to do so, this candidate has expressed $f'(x)$ in a form without negative indices.

(b)

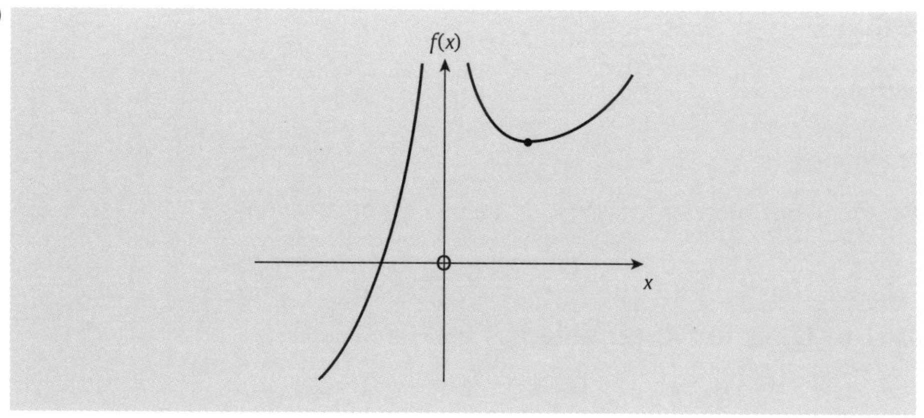

The turning point occurs when

$$1 - \frac{2}{x^3} = 0$$

$$\therefore \quad x^3 = 2$$

$$\therefore \quad x = 1.3$$

The function is increasing for $x < 0$ and for $x > 1.3$.

e $x < 0$ is correct and gains 1 mark. The second interval is identified and a correct method used to find the value of x at which the turning point occurs, for a second mark. But the answer 1.3 is not accurate. An accurate answer is $x > 2^{\frac{1}{3}}$.

Question 5

Find the gradient of the curve $y = x + \ln x$ at the point $P(1, 1)$. Hence, find the equation of the tangent to the curve at the point P. (5 marks)

■ ■ ■

Answer to Question 5: candidate A (4 out of 5 marks)

$$y = x + \ln x$$

$$\therefore \quad \frac{dy}{dx} = 1 + \frac{1}{x}$$

At P, the gradient is $1 + 1 = 2$. The tangent is $y - y_1 = m(x - x_1)$, i.e. $y - 1 = 2(x - 1)$.

e This is correct, for 3 marks, but 1 mark is lost for not simplifying the equation of the tangent further.

■ ■ ■

Answer to Question 5: candidate B (5 out of 5 marks)

$$y = x + \ln x$$

$$\frac{dy}{dx} = 1 + \frac{1}{x}$$

At P, $x = 1$

$$\frac{dy}{dx} = 2$$

The tangent at P is given by

$$y = 2x + c$$

Since $x = 1$, $y = 1$

$$1 = 2 + c$$

$$\therefore \quad c = -1$$

The equation of the tangent is $y = 2x - 1$.

e This is a different method and slightly long-winded, but correct, for full marks.

Question 6

A curve C has equation $y = (x + 1)e^{-x}$.

(a) Determine $\frac{dy}{dx}$ and $\frac{d^2y}{dx^2}$ as functions of x. (4 marks)

(b) Find the coordinates of
(i) the stationary point on C and determine its nature (4 marks)
(ii) the point of inflexion on C (2 marks)

(c) Sketch the graph of C, indicating clearly any intersection points with the axes and the nature of the curve as $x \to +\infty$. (3 marks)

(d) Determine the area enclosed by C, the x-axis and the ordinate $x = 1$. (5 marks)

■ ■ ■

Answer to Question 6: candidate A (6 out of 18 marks)

(a)

$$y = xe^{-x} + e^{-x}$$

$$\therefore \quad \frac{dy}{dx} = xe^{-x} + e^{-x} + e^{-x}$$

$$= xe^{-x} + 2e^{-x}$$

$$\frac{d^2y}{dx^2} = xe^{-x} + e^{-x} + 2e^{-x}$$

$$= xe^{-x} + 3e^{-x}$$

In the case of the first differential, this candidate uses the product rule, for 1 mark, but differentiates e^{-x} incorrectly (the differential of e^{-x} is $-e^{-x}$). Using the incorrect answer for the first derivative, the candidate once again applies the product rule (which is correct, for 1 mark) but differentiates e^{-x} incorrectly.

(b) (i) Put $\frac{dy}{dx} = 0$

$$xe^{-x} + 2e^{-x} = 0$$

$$x + 2 = 0$$

$$x = -2$$

The method is correct, i.e. $\frac{dy}{dx} = 0$. Even though the candidate has used an incorrect $\frac{dy}{dx}$, 1 mark is awarded for putting $\frac{dy}{dx} = 0$. This candidate has not attempted to find the corresponding y value, nor the nature of the stationary point.

(ii) Put $\frac{d^2y}{dx^2} = 0$

$$xe^{-x} + 3e^{-x} = 0$$

$$x + 3 = 0$$

$$x = -3$$

The method is correct, i.e. $\frac{d^2y}{dx^2} = 0$, so 1 mark is gained. Once again, the candidate has used an incorrect $\frac{d^2y}{dx^2}$.

(c)

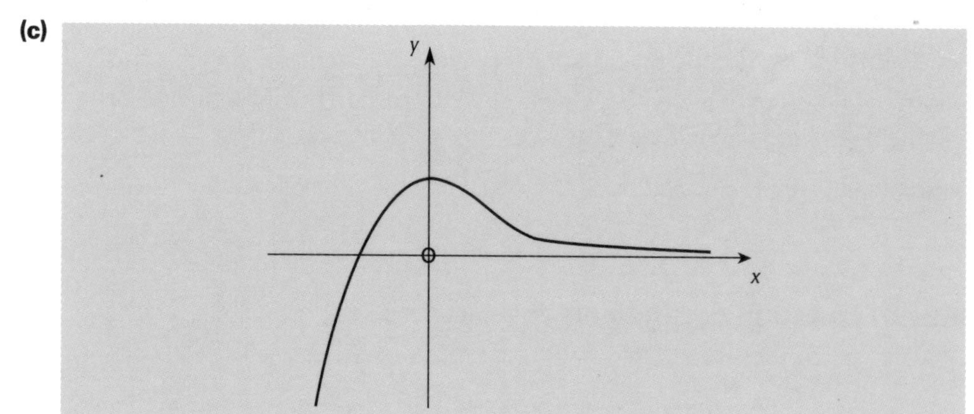

The sketch graph is correct, but there is no indication of the intersection points with the axes, so only 1 mark is awarded.

(d) The area is

$$\int_0^1 (x+1)e^{-x}\,dx = \left[\left(\frac{x^2}{2} + x\right)e^{-x}\right]_0^1$$

$$= 1.55$$

e The definite integral written down is correct, which gains 1 mark. The integration is incorrect and the candidate has not used a correct method. The evaluation is incorrect even for the candidate's answer.

■ ■ ■

Answer to Question 6: candidate B (16 out of 18 marks)

(a) $y = (x+1)e^{-x}$

$$\frac{dy}{dx} = (x+1)\,(-e^{-x}) + e^{-x}.1$$

$$= -xe^{-x}$$

$$\frac{d^2y}{dx^2} = -x\,(-e^{-x}) + e^{-x}(-1)$$

$$= xe^{-x} - e^{-x}$$

e The first and second derivatives are correct, for 4 marks.

(b) (i) At a stationary point,

$$\frac{dy}{dx} = -xe^{-x} = 0$$

$$\therefore \quad x = 0$$

When $x = 0$,

$$\frac{d^2y}{dx^2} = 0 - 1 = -1$$

This is negative, so the stationary point is a maximum.

e This is correct, for 3 marks, but the candidate has not found the corresponding *y* value.

(ii) For the point of inflexion

$$\frac{d^2y}{dx^2} = xe^{-x} - e^{-x} = 0$$

$$\therefore \quad e^{-x}\,(x-1) = 0$$

$$\therefore \quad x = 1$$

This is correct, for 1 mark, but again the candidate has failed to find the corresponding y value.

(c)

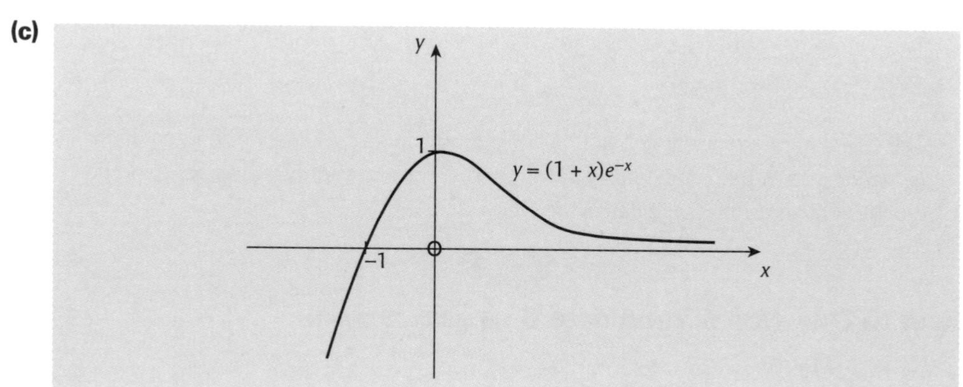

This is correct, for 3 marks.

(d) The area is given by

$$\int_0^1 (x+1)e^{-x}dx$$

Using integration by parts,

$$\begin{aligned}\int (x+1)\,e^{-x}dx &= (x+1)e^{-x} + \int e^{-x}dx \\ &= (x+1)(-e^{x}) - \int_0^1 (-e^{-x})\,dx \\ &= -e^{-x}(x+1) - e^{-x} + c \\ &= -xe^{-x} - 2e^{-x} + c\end{aligned}$$

Therefore,

$$\begin{aligned}\int_0^1 (x+1)e^{-x}\,dx &= [-xe^{-x} - 2e^{-x}]_0^1 \\ &= (-e^{-1} - 2e^{-1}) - (-2) \\ &= -3e^{-1} + 2\end{aligned}$$

This is correct, for full marks.

Question 7

Shown below is the graph of $y = x\sqrt{1+x}$. The point $(a, 0)$ is where the curve intersects the x-axis. The point (p, q) is the minimum turning point on the curve.

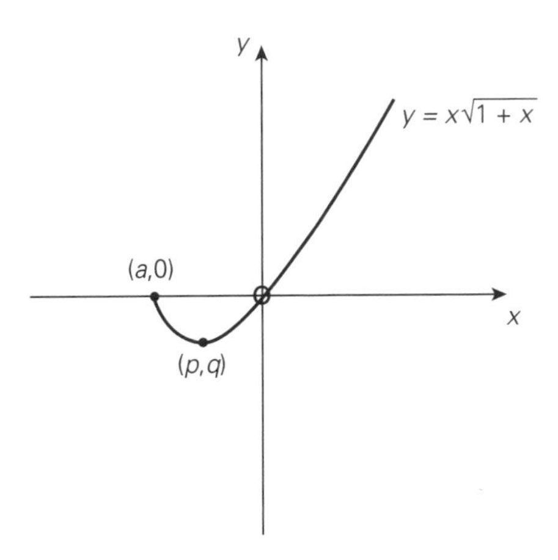

(a) Find the value of a and explain why y is not defined for $x < a$. (4 marks)

(b) Show that

$$\frac{dy}{dx} = \frac{1}{2\sqrt{1+x}}(3x+2) \qquad \text{(4 marks)}$$

(c) Determine the values of p and q. (3 marks)

Answer to Question 7: candidate A (3 out of 11 marks)

(a) The intersection with the x-axis is when $x\sqrt{1+x} = 0$. Squaring both sides gives

$$x^2(1+x) = 0$$

$$x = 0 \text{ or } x = -1$$

y is not defined because the square root is negative.

e Although long-winded, this method gives the two possible values for a. However, the candidate doesn't eliminate $x = 0$ and state $a = -1$, and so scores just 1 mark. The explanation for why y is not defined is not precise since 'the square root is negative' means $-\sqrt{}$. The candidate actually means that the term under the square root is negative, i.e. $1 + x < 0$, but is not precise. No marks are awarded for this part.

(b) $$y^2 = x^2(1+x) = x^2 + x^3$$

Differentiating gives $2x + 3x^2$ for y^2,

$$\therefore \quad \frac{dy}{dx} = \sqrt{2x+3x^2}$$

The candidate has written $y^2 = x^2(1 + x)$ in an attempt to simplify the expression (i.e. remove the square root), but has not realised the consequences. This is incorrect.

(c) At the turning point,

$$\frac{3x + 2}{2\sqrt{1 + x}} = 0$$

$$\therefore \quad 3x + 2 = 0,$$

$$x = -\tfrac{2}{3}$$

The candidate has sensibly used the answer given in **(b)** to answer this part, rather than his/her own incorrect answer and scores 2 marks. The candidate has failed to find the y-coordinate of the turning point and loses the third mark.

■ ■ ■

Answer to Question 7: candidate B (10 out of 11 marks)

(a) When $y = 0$

$$x\sqrt{1 + x} = 0$$

$$\therefore \quad x = 0 \text{ or } 1 + x = 0$$

$$\therefore \quad x = 0 \text{ or } x = -1$$

$x = 0$ corresponds to the intersection at the origin; $x = -1$ is the other intersection with the x-axis. Therefore, $a = -1$.

When $x < -1$, $(1 + x) < 0$. But when $(1 + x) < 0$, $\sqrt{1 + x}$ is not defined, i.e. y is not defined.

This is correct, for 4 marks.

(b)

$$y = x(1 + x)^{\frac{1}{2}}$$

$$\therefore \quad \frac{dy}{dx} = x.\tfrac{1}{2}(1 + x)^{-\frac{1}{2}} + (1 + x)^{\frac{1}{2}}$$

$$= \frac{x}{2}\frac{1}{\sqrt{1 + x}} + \sqrt{1 + x}$$

This is correct, except for the final rearrangement. The candidate needs to take out a factor of $(1 + x)^{-\frac{1}{2}}$, to give the required form:

$$(1 + x)^{-\frac{1}{2}}\left\{\frac{x}{2} + (1 + x)\right\} = \frac{3x + 2}{\phantom{2\sqrt{1+x}}}$$

3 marks are awarded.

(c) At the turning point,

$$\frac{3x+2}{2\sqrt{1+x}} = 0$$

$$\therefore \quad 3x + 2 = 0$$

$$\therefore \quad x = -\tfrac{2}{3}$$

When $x = -\frac{2}{3}$, $y = -\frac{2}{3}\sqrt{1-\frac{2}{3}} = -\frac{2}{3}\sqrt{\frac{1}{3}} = -\frac{2}{3\sqrt{3}}$. Therefore, $p = -\frac{2}{3}$ and $q = -\frac{2}{3\sqrt{3}}$.

e This candidate sensibly used the answer for $\frac{dy}{dx}$ given in part **(b)** of the question. The solution is correct, for 3 marks.

Question 8

Shown below is the graph of the curve given parametrically by

$x = 2\cos^3 t,\ y = 2\sin^3 t,\ -\pi < t \leqslant \pi$

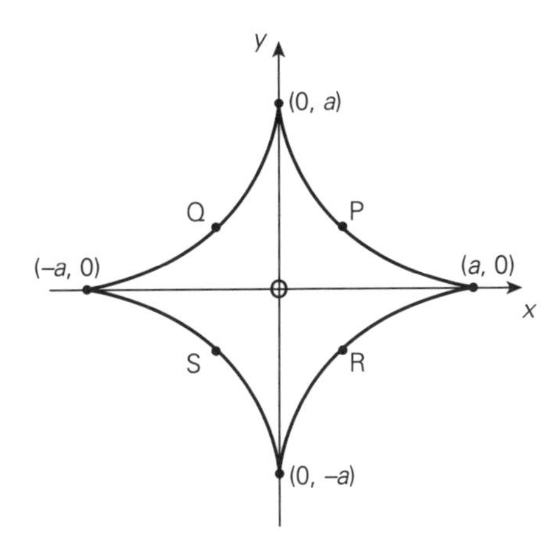

(a) Find the value of the constant a. (3 marks)

(b) Show that $\frac{dy}{dx} = -\tan t$. (4 marks)

(c) At point P, $t = \frac{\pi}{4}$. Find

(i) the gradient of the curve at P (1 mark)

(ii) the equation of the tangent line to the curve at P (4 marks)

(d) Points Q, R and S have t values $\frac{3\pi}{4}, \frac{\pi}{2}, -\frac{3\pi}{4}$. The tangent lines to the curve at each of the points P, Q, R and S meet on the axes to form a square. Using your answer from **(c)**(ii), together with the symmetrical properties of the curve, find the area of the square enclosed by these tangent lines. (3 marks)

■ ■ ■

Answer to Question 8: candidate A (3 out of 15 marks)

(a) $a = 2$

ⓔ Although no explanation is given, this is correct and gains 1 mark for the correct value.

(b) $\frac{dx}{dt} = 6\sin^2 t$

$\frac{dy}{dt} = 6\cos^2 t$

$\frac{dy}{dx} = \frac{6\sin^2 t}{6\cos^2 t} = \tan^2 t$

ⓔ Neither differentiation is correct and this candidate has not applied the method of 'function of a function'. In addition, he/she has not used the chain rule correctly to find $\frac{dy}{dx}$. No marks are awarded.

(c) (i) When $t = \frac{\pi}{4}$

$$\frac{dy}{dx} = -\tan\left(\frac{\pi}{4}\right) = -1$$

ⓔ The candidate has used the version of $\frac{dy}{dx}$ given in the question, which is a good technique, and calculated the gradient correctly. 1 mark is awarded.

(ii) The tangent line is

$$y - \frac{\pi}{4} = -1\left(x - \frac{\pi}{4}\right)$$

$$y = -x + \frac{\pi}{2}$$

ⓔ Although the correct straight line formula is used to find the tangent, for 1 mark, this candidate has taken the parameter value (t) to be the x and y values.

(d) The area is $\left(\frac{\pi}{2}\right)^2 = 2.467$.

ⓔ The final part uses the incorrect value and an incorrect method.

■ ■ ■

Answer to Question 8: candidate B (15 out of 15 marks)

(a) When $y = 0$,

$$2\sin^3 t = 0$$

$$\therefore \quad \sin t = 0$$

$$\therefore \quad t = 0$$

When $t = 0$,

$$x = 2\cos^3(0) = 2$$

Therefore, $a = 2$.

This is clearly explained and correct, for full marks.

(b) $\dfrac{dx}{dt} = 6\cos^2 t(-\sin t) = -6\cos^2 t \sin t$

$\dfrac{dy}{dx} = 6\sin^2 t \cos t$

Now $\dfrac{dy}{dx} = \dfrac{dy}{dt} \times \dfrac{dt}{dx} = 6\sin^2 t\cos t \times \dfrac{1}{-6\cos^2 t \sin t} = -\dfrac{\sin t}{\cos t} = -\tan t$

The candidate has clearly displayed use of the chain rule by writing $\frac{dy}{dx} = \frac{dy}{dt} \times \frac{dt}{dx}$. Full marks are awarded.

(c) (i) When $t = \dfrac{\pi}{4}$,

$$\frac{dy}{dx} = -\tan\left(\frac{\pi}{4}\right) = -1$$

The gradient at P is -1.

(ii) The coordinates of P are

$$x = 2\cos^3\left(\frac{\pi}{4}\right) = 2\left(\frac{1}{\sqrt{2}}\right)^3 = \frac{1}{\sqrt{2}}$$

and

$$y = 2\sin^3\left(\frac{\pi}{4}\right) = 2\left(\frac{1}{\sqrt{2}}\right)^3 = \frac{1}{\sqrt{2}}$$

The tangent line is

$$y - \frac{1}{\sqrt{2}} = -1\left(x - \frac{1}{\sqrt{2}}\right)$$

$$\therefore \quad y = -x + \frac{1}{\sqrt{2}} + \frac{1}{\sqrt{2}}$$

$$\therefore \quad y = -x + \frac{2}{\sqrt{2}}$$

This is very clear and correct, for full marks.

(d) The square can be divided into four triangles:

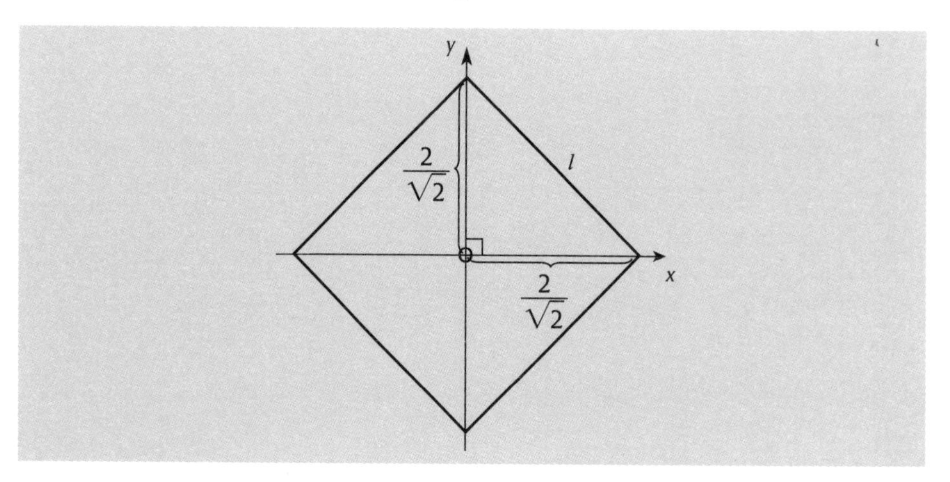

For each triangle,

$$l^2 = \left(\frac{2}{\sqrt{2}}\right)^2 + \left(\frac{2}{\sqrt{2}}\right)^2 = 4$$

$$\therefore \quad l = 2$$

Therefore, the area of the square is 4.

e This is well answered, for 3 marks.

Integration

Question 1

The curve shown has the equation $y = x^3 - 5x^2 + 3x + 9$.

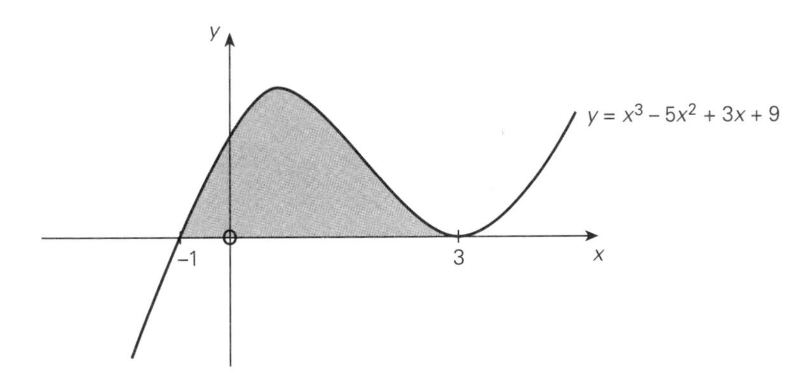

Find the area of the shaded region enclosed by the curve and the x-axis. (4 marks)

■ ■ ■

Answer to Question 1: candidate A (2 out of 4 marks)

$$\int_{-1}^{3} x^3 - 5x^2 + 3x + 9 \, dx = \left[\frac{x^4}{4} - \frac{5x^3}{3} + \frac{3x^2}{2} + 9x\right]_{-1}^{3}$$

$$= 15.75 - 5.58 = 10.17$$

e The definite integral and the integration are correct, for 2 marks. However, the values have been calculated incorrectly. Although the 15.75 is correct, 5.58 is approximated rather than given in fraction form and the sign is incorrect.

■ ■ ■

Answer to Question 1: candidate B (4 out of 4 marks)

$$\int_{-1}^{3} x^3 - 5x^2 + 3x + 9 \, dx = \left[\frac{x^4}{4} - \frac{5x^3}{3} + \frac{3x^2}{2} + 9x\right]_{-1}^{3}$$

$$= \frac{63}{4} - \left(-\frac{67}{12}\right) = \frac{64}{3}$$

e This is correct and the candidate shows the value corresponding to the substitution of each limit, for full marks.

Question 2

The finite region bounded by the curve with equation $y = e^x$, the x-axis and the ordinates $x = 0$, $x = 2$ is rotated through 360° about the x-axis. Using integration, find, in terms of π, the volume of the solid formed. (5 marks)

■ ■ ■

Answer to Question 2: candidate A (1 out of 5 marks)

Volume is $V = \pi \int y^2 \, dx$.

Therefore,

$$V = \pi \int_0^2 e^{x^2} dx = \pi \left[\frac{e^{x^2}}{2} \right]_0^2 = 84.2$$

This candidate gains 1 mark for $V = \pi \int y^2 \, dx$. However, as $y = e^x$, $y^2 = e^{2x}$ (not e^{x^2}). The integration is incorrect for the candidate's function. Also, the answer has not been left in terms of π.

■ ■ ■

Answer to Question 2: candidate B (5 out of 5 marks)

$$V = \pi \int_0^2 (e^x)^2 dx$$

$$= \pi \int_0^2 e^{2x} dx$$

$$= \pi \left[\frac{e^{2x}}{2} \right]_0^2$$

$$= \pi \left(\frac{e^4}{2} - \frac{1}{2} \right)$$

This is correct and the solution shows clearly the different stages of the calculation, for full marks.

Question 3

Find

(a) $\int x^2(x + 1) \, dx$ (3 marks)

(b) $\int \left(\frac{x^2}{2} + \frac{1}{x^2} \right)^2 dx$ (4 marks)

■ ■ ■

Answer to Question 3: candidate A (3 out of 7 marks)

(a) $\int x^2(x+1)\,dx = \int x^3 + x^2\,dx$

$$= \frac{x^4}{4} + \frac{x^3}{3}$$

This answer is correct, except for the missing constant of integration. 2 marks are awarded.

(b) $\int \left(\frac{x^2}{2} + \frac{1}{x^2}\right)^2 dx = \int \frac{x^4}{4} + \frac{1}{x^4}\,dx$

$$= \frac{x^5}{20} + \frac{1}{5x^5}$$

This candidate has squared the brackets incorrectly, missing out the cross-terms. 1 mark is awarded for correctly integrating $\frac{x^4}{4}$. However, the candidate has integrated the term $\frac{1}{x^4}$ incorrectly, i.e. failed to write it as x^{-4} and then apply the integration rule. The constant of integration is missing.

■ ■ ■

Answer to Question 3: candidate B (7 out of 7 marks)

(a) $\int x^2(x+1)\,dx = \int x^3 + x^2\,dx$

$$= \frac{x^4}{4} + \frac{x^3}{3} + c$$

This is correct, for 3 marks.

(b) $\int \left(\frac{x^2}{2} + \frac{1}{x^2}\right)^2 dx = \int \left(\frac{x^2}{2} + \frac{1}{x^2}\right)\left(\frac{x^2}{2} + \frac{1}{x^2}\right) dx$

$$= \int \frac{x^4}{4} + \frac{1}{2} + \frac{1}{2} + \frac{1}{x^4}\,dx$$

$$= \frac{x^5}{20} + x + \frac{x^{-3}}{(-3)} + c$$

This is correct and gains full marks. The final answer could be written as

$$\frac{x^5}{20} + x - \frac{1}{3x^3} + c$$

Question 4

The diagram shows the line $y = x + 2$ and the curve with equation $y = 6 + x - x^2$.

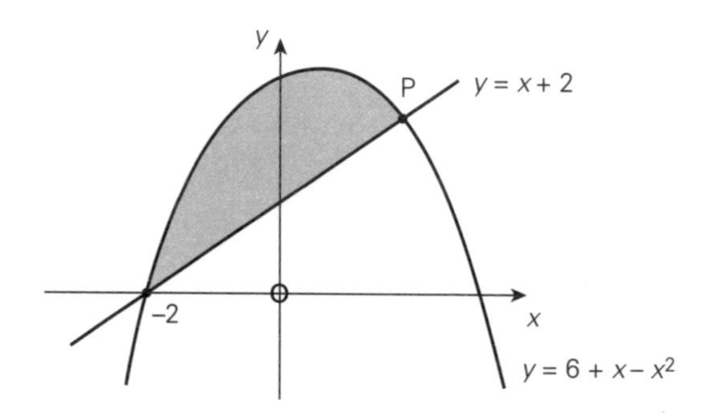

(a) Find the coordinates of point P. (2 marks)

(b) Calculate the exact area of the shaded region enclosed by the curve and the line. (5 marks)

■ ■ ■

Answer to Question 4: candidate A (2 out of 7 marks)

(a) $x + 2 = 6 + x - x^2$

$\therefore \quad x^2 = 4$

$\therefore \quad x = 2$

When $x = 2$, $y = 2 + 2 = 4$.

e The coordinates of P are correct, for 1 mark, but in solving the equation $x^2 = 4$, it is unclear whether the candidate has eliminated the possibility of $x = -2$ or ignored it!

(b) Area under curve:

$$\int_{-2}^{2} 6 + x - x^2 \, dx = \left[6x + \frac{x^2}{2} - \frac{x^3}{3}\right]_{-2}^{2}$$

$$= 18.67$$

The area of the triangle is $\frac{1}{2}.4.4 = 8$.

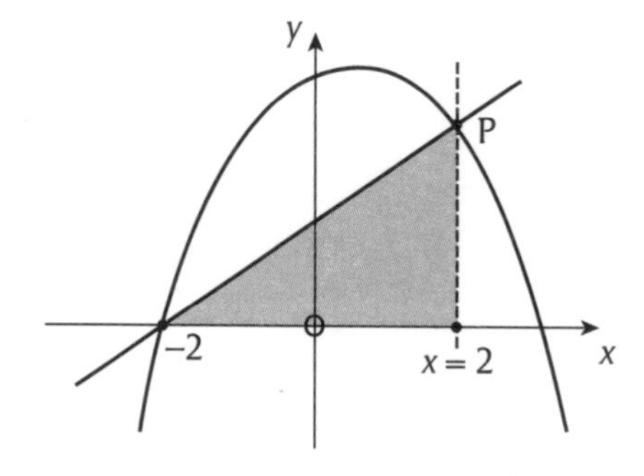

The area of the shaded region is $18.67 - 8 = 10.67$.

e This candidate has tackled the area problem in an unnecessarily complicated way. In doing so, he/she has only subtracted from 18.67 the area of the triangle and has missed subtracting the area under the curve between $x = 2$ and $x = 3$. The definite integral, integration and use of limits gain 1 mark. The answer of 18.67, to the definite integral, gains no marks as it is not exact (the question asks for the exact area).

■ ■ ■

Answer to Question 4: candidate B (6 out of 7 marks)

(a) At the intersection,

$$6 + x - x^2 = x + 2$$

$$\therefore \quad x^2 = 4$$

$$\therefore \quad x = \pm 2$$

$x = -2$ corresponds to the intersection with the x-axis. The x coordinate of P is 2 and the y coordinate is given by $y = 2 + 2 = 4$. Therefore, P is $(2, 4)$.

e The coordinates of P are correct, for 2 marks.

(b) The area is given by

$$\int_{-2}^{2} 6 + x - x^2 \, dx - \int_{-2}^{2} x + 2 \, dx$$

$$= \int_{-2}^{2} 8 - x^2 \, dx$$

$$= \left[8x - \frac{x^3}{3} \right]_{-2}^{2}$$

$$= \frac{40}{3} - \left(-\frac{40}{3} \right)$$

$$= \frac{80}{3}$$

The area of the shaded region is $\frac{80}{3}$ square units.

e The definite integral in the first line is correct, which gains 1 mark. However, the candidate has made a slip with the negative sign as the resulting definite integral should be $\int_{-2}^{2} 4 - x^2 \, dx$ and not $\int_{-2}^{2} 8 - x^2 \, dx$. Using the candidate's simplified integral, all the working is then correct, which gains a further 3 marks.

Question 5

A radioactive material is known to decay at a rate proportional to the amount present and is modelled by the differential equation

$$\frac{dM}{dt} = kM$$

where M denotes the amount of material present at time t.

(a) Solve the differential equation and show that $M = Ae^{kt}$, where A is a constant.
(5 marks)

(b) Given that initially there is 60 milligrams of the material present and that after 1 hour there is 52 milligrams of the material present, find the value of the constants A and k.
(3 marks)

(c) Find the time at which the material has decayed to one quarter of its initial mass.
(4 marks)

■ ■ ■

Answer to Question 5: candidate A (4 out of 12 marks)

(a) $$\int \frac{dM}{dt} = \int kM$$

$$\therefore \quad M = kMt$$

$$\therefore \quad M = Ae^{kt}$$

This is incorrect. This candidate has not separated the variables. Line 3 of the working is simply a copy of the final answer given in the question!

(b) $60 = Ae^0 \Rightarrow A = 60$

When $t = 1, M = 52$

$$52 = 60e^k$$

$$\therefore \quad k = \frac{52}{60e} = 0.32$$

Constant A is correct, which gains 1 mark. Constant k is incorrect as this candidate does not know how to solve for k when it is a power of e. However, 1 mark is gained for the initial substitution.

(c) $$15 = 60e^{0.32t}$$

$$\therefore \quad 0.32t = \frac{15}{60e}$$

$$\therefore \quad t = 0.287$$

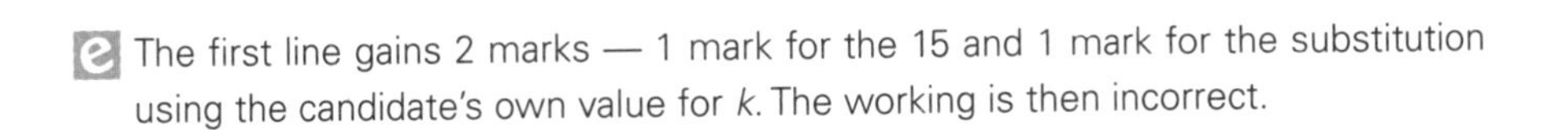

The first line gains 2 marks — 1 mark for the 15 and 1 mark for the substitution using the candidate's own value for k. The working is then incorrect.

■ ■ ■

Answer to Question 5: candidate B (11 out of 12 marks)

(a) $$\int \frac{\mathrm{d}M}{M} = \int k\,\mathrm{d}t$$

$$\therefore \quad \ln M = kt + c$$

$$\therefore \quad M = e^{kt+c}$$

$$\therefore \quad M = Ae^{kt}$$

This is correct. However, the step from $M = e^{kt+c}$ to $M = Ae^{kt}$ is missing, which loses 1 mark. The missing step is:

$M = e^{kt}e^{c}$ and since e^{c} is a constant we can write $A = e^{c}$

$$\therefore \quad M = Ae^{kt}$$

(b) $t = 0, M = 60 \Rightarrow A = 60$

$t = 1, M = 52$ gives

$$60e^{k} = 52$$

$$\therefore \quad e^{k} = \frac{52}{60}$$

$$\therefore \quad k = \ln\left(\frac{13}{15}\right)$$

This is correct, for 3 marks.

(c) When $M = \frac{1}{4}(60) = 15$, this gives

$$60e^{t\ln\left(\frac{13}{15}\right)} = 15$$

$$\therefore \quad e^{t\ln\left(\frac{13}{15}\right)} = \frac{15}{60} = \frac{1}{4}$$

$$\therefore \quad t\ln\left(\frac{13}{15}\right) = \ln\left(\frac{1}{4}\right)$$

$$\therefore \quad t = 9.69 \text{ hours}$$

This is correct, for 4 marks.

Question 6

(a) Show that

$$\frac{1}{1-x} - \frac{2}{1+3x} \equiv \frac{5x-1}{(1-x)(1+3x)}$$

(2 marks)

(b) Hence show that

$$\int_0^{\frac{1}{2}} \frac{5x-1}{(1-x)(1+3x)}\,dx = \tfrac{1}{3}(5\ln 2 - 2\ln 5)$$

(6 marks)

■ ■ ■

Answer to Question 6: candidate A (4 out of 8 marks)

(a) Using partial fractions,

$$\frac{5x-1}{(1-x)(1+3x)} \equiv \frac{A}{1-x} + \frac{B}{1+3x}$$

$$5x - 1 \equiv A(1+3x) + B(1-x)$$

When $x = 1, 4 = 4A \Rightarrow A = 1$

When $x = 0, -1 = A + B \Rightarrow B = -2$

Therefore,

$$\frac{1}{1-x} - \frac{2}{1+3x} \equiv \frac{5x-1}{(1-x)(1+3x)}$$

e This candidate has not read the question carefully and simply opted for partial fractions, which is time-consuming and a lot of work for just 2 marks. However, the answer is correct, and 2 marks are awarded.

(b)
$$\int_0^{\frac{1}{2}} \frac{5x-1}{(1-x)(1+3x)}\,dx = \int_0^{\frac{1}{2}} \frac{1}{1-x} - \frac{2}{1+3x}\,dx$$

$$= \Big[\ln(1-x) - 2\ln(1+3x)\Big]_0^{\frac{1}{2}}$$

$$= \ln\left(\frac{1}{2}\right) - 2\ln\left(2\frac{1}{2}\right) - 0$$

$$= 2\ln\left(\frac{\frac{1}{2}}{2\frac{1}{2}}\right) = 2\ln\left(\frac{1}{5}\right)$$

e This method of using the split fraction from **(a)** is correct and gains 1 mark. Each of the integrals is incorrect, as the candidate has ignored the coefficient of the

x term (i.e. -1 and 3) in each denominator when using the log rule. Use of limits with the candidate's answer is correct, which gains a second mark. The log manipulation is incorrect.

■ ■ ■

Answer to Question 6: candidate B (7 out of 8 marks)

(a) $$\frac{1}{1-x} - \frac{2}{1+3x} = \frac{(1+3x) - 2(1-x)}{(1-x)(1+3x)}$$

$$= \frac{5x-1}{(1-x)(1+3x)}$$

This is correct, for 2 marks. This candidate has realised that although this may look like a 'split into partial fractions' question, it is simply writing two algebraic fractions as one, using a common denominator.

(b) $$\int_0^{\frac{1}{2}} \frac{5x-1}{(1-x)(1+3x)}\,dx = \int_0^{\frac{1}{2}} \frac{1}{1-x} - \frac{2}{1+3x}\,dx$$

$$= \left[-\ln|1-x| - \frac{2}{3}\ln|1+3x|\right]_0^{\frac{1}{2}}$$

$$= \left(-\ln\left(\frac{1}{2}\right) - \frac{2}{3}\ln\left(\frac{5}{2}\right)\right) - (0)$$

$$= -\ln 1 - \ln 2 - \frac{2}{3}(\ln 5 - \ln 2)$$

$$= -\ln 2 - \frac{2}{3}\ln 5 + \frac{2}{3}\ln 2$$

$$= -\frac{1}{3}\ln 2 - \frac{2}{3}\ln 5$$

This is almost correct, for 5 marks. The candidate's answer does not agree with the question because of a slip with a negative sign, so 1 mark is lost. The correct manipulation is

$$\left(-\ln\left(\frac{1}{2}\right) - \frac{2}{3}\ln\left(\frac{5}{2}\right)\right) - (0) = -(\ln 1 - \ln 2) - \frac{2}{3}(\ln 5 - \ln 2)$$

$$= \ln 2 - \frac{2}{3}\ln 5 + \frac{2}{3}\ln 2$$

$$= \frac{5}{3}\ln 2 - \frac{2}{3}\ln 5$$

$$= \frac{1}{3}(5\ln 2 - 2\ln 5)$$

Question 7

The area enclosed by the curve $y = \sin x + \cos x$, the x-axis and the lines $x = 0$ and $x = \frac{\pi}{2}$, is rotated through 360° about the x-axis. Find the volume of the solid generated, leaving your answer in terms of π. (6 marks)

■ ■ ■

Answer to Question 7: candidate A (2 out of 6 marks)

$$V = \pi \int y^2 \, dx$$

$$= \pi \int_0^{\frac{\pi}{2}} (\sin^2 x + \cos^2 x) \, dx$$

$$= \pi \int_0^{\frac{\pi}{2}} 1 \, dx$$

$$= \pi \Big[x \Big]_0^{\frac{\pi}{2}}$$

$$= \pi \left(\frac{\pi}{2} \right) = \frac{\pi^2}{2}$$

e The first line gains 1 mark for method, but the second does not as this candidate has made the common error of missing the cross-terms in the expansion of $(\sin x + \cos x)^2$. Integration of the candidate's y^2 is correct but gains no marks. Use of limits is correct, which gains 1 mark. 2 marks are awarded.

■ ■ ■

Answer to Question 7: candidate B (6 out of 6 marks)

$$V = \pi \int_0^{\frac{\pi}{2}} (\sin x + \cos x)^2 \, dx$$

$$= \pi \int_0^{\frac{\pi}{2}} \sin^2 x + 2 \sin x \cos x + \cos^2 x \, dx$$

$$= \pi \int_0^{\frac{\pi}{2}} 1 + 2 \sin x \cos x \, dx$$

Now, $\int 2 \sin x \cos x \, dx = \int 2 \cos x (\sin x)^1 \, dx = \frac{2(\sin x)^2}{2} + c = \sin^2 x + c$

Therefore,

$$V = \pi \Big[x + \sin^2 x \Big]_0^{\frac{\pi}{2}}$$

$= \pi\left(\frac{\pi}{2} + 1\right) - 0$

e This is correct, for 6 marks. It is worth noting that the interesting integral in this question is $\int 2\sin x\cos x\,dx$. The candidate could have written this as

$$\int \sin 2x\,dx = -\frac{\cos 2x}{2} + c$$

which would give the same numerical answer for the volume. A third alternative, similar to the method used by the candidate, is:

$$\int 2\sin x\cos x\,dx = \int 2\sin x(\cos x)^1\,dx$$

$$= -\frac{2(\cos x)^2}{2} + c$$

$$= -\cos^2 x + c$$

The step from line 1 to line 2 of working is using the 'function of a function' rule.

Question 8

(a) Starting with the identity $\cos 2A \equiv \cos^2 A - \sin^2 A$, show that

$\sin^2 A \equiv \frac{1}{2}(1 - \cos 2A)$ (2 marks)

(b) Find $\int \sin^2 x\,dx$ (3 marks)

(c) Using the substitution $x = \sin t$, show that

$$\int_0^{\frac{1}{2}} \frac{x^2}{\sqrt{1 - x^2}}\,dx = \frac{\pi}{12} - \frac{\sqrt{3}}{8}$$ (8 marks)

■ ■ ■

Answer to Question 8: candidate A (4 out of 13 marks)

(a) $\sin^2 A = \cos^2 A - \cos 2A$

$= 1 - \sin^2 A - \cos 2A$

$\therefore \quad 2\sin^2 A = 1 - \cos 2A$

$\therefore \quad \sin^2 A = \frac{1}{2}(1 - \cos 2A)$

e This gains full marks.

(b) $\int \sin^2 x\,dx = \frac{\sin^3 x}{3} + c$

e This is incorrect and one of the most common errors that occurs in integrating trigonometric functions. This candidate has not realised that the first part of the question will help with this part.

(c) $$\int_0^{\frac{1}{2}} \frac{\sin^2 t}{\sqrt{1-\sin^2 t}}\,dt = \int_0^{\frac{1}{2}} \frac{\sin^2 t}{\sqrt{\cos^2 t}}\,dt$$

$$= \int_0^{\frac{1}{2}} \frac{\sin^2 t}{\cos t}\,dt$$

e 1 mark is awarded for substituting $x = \sin t$, and 1 mark for simplifying the denominator to $\cos t$. The candidate has simply replaced dx with dt, which is incorrect, and has failed to complete the question.

■ ■ ■

Answer to Question 8: candidate B (9 out of 13 marks)

(a) $$\cos 2A \equiv \cos^2 A - \sin^2 A$$

$$\equiv (1 - \sin^2 A) - \sin^2 A$$

$$\equiv 1 - 2\sin^2 A$$

$$\therefore \quad \sin^2 A \equiv \tfrac{1}{2}(1 - \cos 2A)$$

e The identity is correct, for 2 marks.

(b) $$\int \sin^2 x\,dx = \int \tfrac{1}{2}(1 - \cos 2x)\,dx$$

$$= \frac{1}{2}\left[x - \frac{\sin 2x}{2}\right] + c$$

e This is correct, for 3 marks.

(c) If $x = \sin t$, then $\dfrac{dx}{dt} = \cos t \Rightarrow dx = \cos t\,dt$. Substituting $x = \sin t$,

$$\int_0^{\frac{1}{2}} \frac{x^2}{\sqrt{1-x^2}}\,dx = \int \frac{\sin^2 t}{\sqrt{1-\sin^2 t}} \cos t\,dt$$

$$= \int \frac{\sin^2 t \cos t}{\sqrt{\cos^2 t}}\,dt$$

$$= \int \sin^2 t\,dt$$

$$= \left[\frac{1}{2}\left(x - \frac{\sin 2x}{2}\right)\right]_0^{\frac{1}{2}}$$

$$= \frac{1}{2}\left(\frac{1}{2} - \frac{\sin 1}{2}\right) = 0.04 \text{ to } 2\,\text{d.p.}$$

This is not correct. The error occurs when the candidate integrates $\sin^2 t$ and gives the answer in the variable x. At this point, the candidate should have written

$$\int \sin^2 t\,dt = \frac{1}{2}\left(t - \frac{\sin 2t}{2}\right)$$

and then changed the x limits of 0 and $\frac{1}{2}$ to t limits. When $x = 0$, $t = 0$. When $x = \frac{1}{2}$, $t = \frac{\pi}{6}$. This gives

$$\int_0^{\frac{1}{2}} \frac{x^2}{1\sqrt{-x^2}}\,dx = \left[\frac{1}{2}t - \frac{\sin 2t}{2}\right]_0^{\frac{\pi}{6}} \quad \text{(4 marks)}$$

Nevertheless, 4 marks are awarded: 1 mark for $\frac{dx}{dt}$, 1 mark for substituting $x = \sin t$ correctly, 1 mark for simplifying $\sqrt{1 - \sin^2 t}$ and 1 mark for $\int \sin^2 t\,dt$.

Question 9

(a) Use integration by parts to find $\int (x + 1) \ln x\,dx$. (4 marks)

(b) Hence show that the area of the shaded region bounded by the curve $y = (x + 1)\ln x$, the x-axis and the line $x = e$, is given by $\frac{1}{4}(e^2 + 5)$. (3 marks)

■ ■ ■

Answer to Question 9: candidate A (5 out of 7 marks)

(a) Differentiate $(x + 1)$ and integrate $\ln x$. Using integration by parts gives

$$(x + 1)\int \ln x\,dx - \int \left(\int \ln x\right)dx$$

Try the functions the other way round. Differentiate $\ln x$ and integrate $(x + 1)$:

$$\ln x\,\frac{(x+1)^2}{2} - \int \frac{(x+1)^2}{2}\,\frac{1}{x}\,dx = \ln x\,\frac{(x+1)^2}{2} - \int \frac{(x+1)^2}{2x}\,dx$$

$$= \ln x\,\frac{(x+1)^2}{2} - \int \frac{x^2 + 2x + 1}{2x}\,dx$$

$$= \ln x\,\frac{(x+1)^2}{2} - \int \frac{x}{2} + 1 + \frac{1}{2x}\,dx$$

$$= \ln x\,\frac{(x+1)^2}{2} - \left(\frac{x^2}{4} + x + \frac{1}{2}\ln x\right)$$

This is an interesting solution as this candidate has integrated $(x + 1)$ in a correct but unusual way. The final answer is correct. Although it could be simplified one step further, it gains full marks.

(b) The area is

$$\int_1^e (x+1)\ln x\,dx = \left[\ln x\,\frac{(x+1)^2}{2} - \left(\frac{x^2}{4} + x + \frac{1}{2}\ln x\right)\right]_1^e$$

$$= \left(\ln e\,\frac{(e+1)^2}{2} - \left(\frac{e^2}{4} + e + \frac{1}{2}\ln e\right)\right) - 0$$

$$= \frac{(e+1)^2}{2} - \left(\frac{e^2}{4+e}\right)$$

$$= \frac{1}{4}(e^2 + 5)$$

e The second part gains 1 mark for the definite integral as the area but no marks for the use of limits as use of the limit $x = 1$ does not generate a zero term when substituted. The candidate has simply written down the final answer as that which appears in the question.

■ ■ ■

Answer to Question 9: candidate B (7 out of 7 marks)

(a) $\int u.\frac{dv}{dx} = uv - \int v.\frac{du}{dx}$

Let $u = \ln x$ and $\frac{dv}{dx} = (x+1)$, then

$$\int (x+1)\ln x\,dx = \left(\frac{x^2}{2} + x\right)\ln x - \int \left(\frac{x^2}{2} + x\right).\frac{1}{x}dx$$

$$= \left(\frac{x^2}{2} + x\right)\ln x - \int \left(\frac{x}{2} + 1\right)dx$$

$$= \left(\frac{x^2}{2} + 1\right)\ln x - \left(\frac{x^2}{4+x}\right) + c$$

e This is a very clear solution, for 4 marks.

(b) The area of the region is

$$\int_1^e (x+1)\ln x\,dx = \left[\left(\frac{x^2}{2} + 1\right)\ln x - \left(\frac{x^2}{4} + x\right)\right]_1^e$$

$$= \left(\frac{e^2}{2} + 1\right)\ln e - \left(\frac{e^2}{4} + e\right) - \left(-\frac{1}{4} + 1\right)$$

$$= \frac{1}{4}(e^2 + 5)$$

e This is correct, for 3 marks. This candidate could have put in an additional line of working showing the simplification to $\frac{1}{4}(e^2 + 5)$.

Numerical methods

Question 1

The graph of $f(x) = e^x - x$ is shown below.

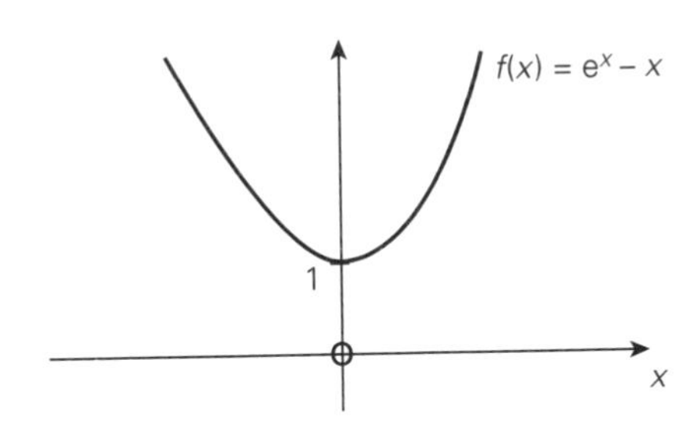

(a) Sketch the graph of $g(x) = e^x - x - 2$, indicating clearly the intersection with the y-axis. (2 marks)

(b) Use your graph from **(a)** to deduce the number of intersections of the graphs of $y = e^x$ and $y = x + 2$. (2 marks)

(c) Given that α and β are the x-coordinates of these points of intersection, show that

$$-2 < \alpha < -1 \text{ and } 1 < \beta < 2$$

(4 marks)

■ ■ ■

Answer to Question 1: candidate A (2 out of 8 marks)

(a)

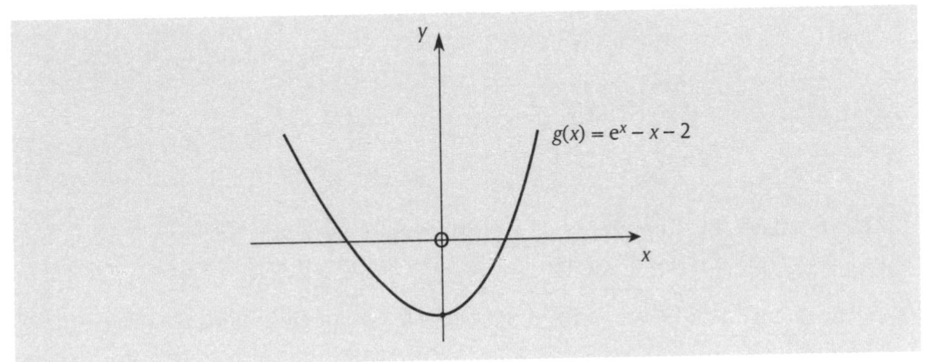

The sketch is correct, for 1 mark, but fails to indicate the intersection with the y-axis.

(b) Two intersections

Two intersections gains 1 mark, but there is no explanation.

(c) The graph of $g(x)$ intersects the x-axis between $x = -1$ and $x = -2$, and between $x = 1$ and $x = 2$.

The final sentence says nothing different from the information given in the question. This gains no marks.

■ ■ ■

Answer to Question 1: candidate B (7 out of 8 marks)

(a)

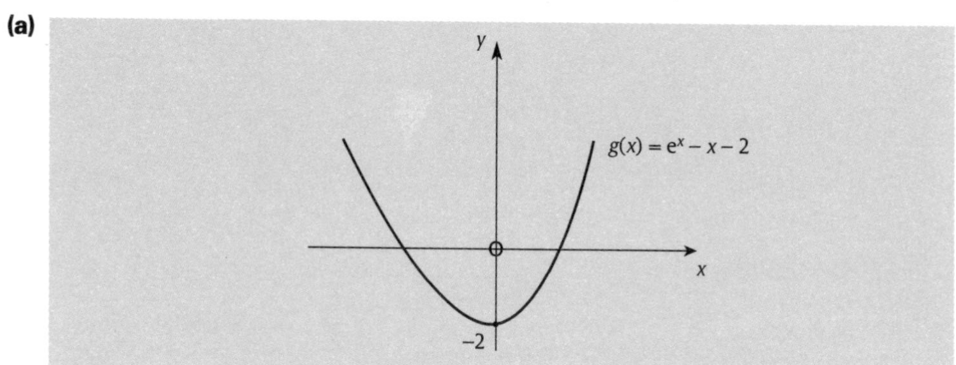

This is correct and shows the intersection with the y-axis clearly, for 2 marks.

(b) The graph of $g(x)$ intersects the x-axis twice and this is where $g(x) = 0$. When $g(x) = 0$,

$$e^x - x - 2 = 0$$

i.e. $$e^x = x + 2$$

Two intersections with the x-axis tell us that the graphs of e^x and $x + 2$ intersect at two points.

This is a correct deduction and explanation, for 2 marks.

(c)

x	-2	-1	1	2
$g(x)$	0.135	−0.632	−0.281	3.389

This table shows that the graph of $g(x)$ intersects the x-axis between $x = -2$ and $x = -1$, and also between $x = 1$ and $x = 2$.

This is correct, but the link to **(b)** is missing, i.e. linking the fact that the x-coordinates of the points where the graph of $g(x)$ intersects the x-axis are in fact the solutions of the equation $e^x = x + 2$. 3 marks are awarded.

Question 2

This sector of a circle of radius r subtends an angle of θ radians at the centre O.

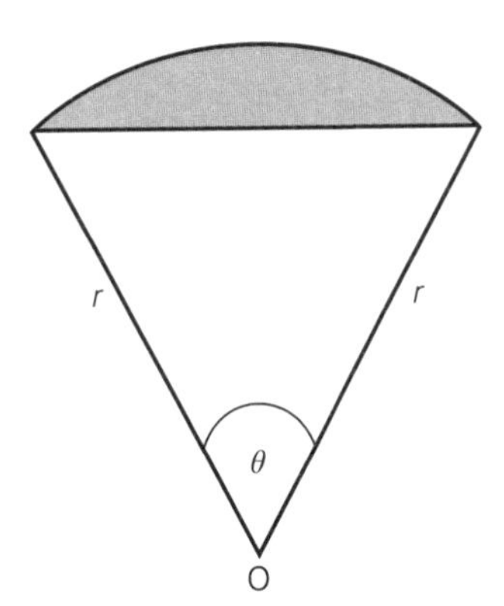

(a) Show that the area A, of the shaded part, is given by

$$A = \frac{r^2}{2}(\theta - \sin\theta)$$ (3 marks)

(b) Given that the radius of the circle is 1 unit and the area A is 1 square unit, show that θ satisfies $\theta - \sin\theta - 2 = 0$. (1 mark)

(c) By letting $f(\theta) = \theta - \sin\theta - 2$ and considering $f(2)$ and $f(3)$, deduce that there exists a root α of the equation in **(b)** such that $2 < \alpha < 3$. (3 marks)

(d) Using Newton–Raphson, together with a suitable initial value, find the value of α correct to three decimal places, showing all iterations. (5 marks)

Answer to Question 2: candidate A (4 out of 12 marks)

(a) The area of the sector is $\frac{\theta}{360°}\pi r^2$.

The area of the triangle is $\frac{1}{2}r^2\sin\theta$.

The shaded area is

$$A = \frac{\theta}{360°}\pi r^2 - \frac{1}{2}r^2\sin\theta$$

$$= \frac{r^2}{2}\left(\frac{\theta\pi}{360} - \sin\theta\right)$$

This candidate has not read the question carefully enough; it states that θ is in radians and yet the candidate uses the sector formula where θ is measured in degrees. 2 marks are awarded.

(b) $$1 = \frac{1}{2}(\theta - \sin\theta)$$

$$\therefore \quad \theta - \sin\theta = 2$$

$$\therefore \quad \theta - \sin\theta - 2 = 0$$

This is correct; the candidate has used the expression for A given in the question. 1 mark is awarded.

(c) $f(2) = 2 - \sin 2 - 2 = -0.0348$

$f(3) = 3 - \sin 3 - 2 = 0.9476$

The change of sign means that there is a root.

The candidate has used degrees instead of radians. It is by chance that there is a change of sign. 1 mark is gained for the deduction using the candidate's own values for (2) and (3).

(d) $x_{r+1} = x_r - \dfrac{f(x_r)}{f'(x_r)}$

The root is 2.554.

The candidate quotes the correct NR formula but makes no attempt to write down the function and its derivative. The answer is correct and gains 1 mark.

■ ■ ■

Answer to Question 2: candidate B (12 out of 12 marks)

(a)

$$A = \frac{\theta}{2\pi}\pi r^2 - \frac{1}{2}r^2 \sin\theta$$

$$= \frac{\theta r^2}{2} - \frac{1}{2}r^2 \sin\theta$$

$$\therefore \quad A = \frac{r^2}{2}(\theta - \sin\theta)$$

This is correct and clear, for full marks.

(b) If $r = 1$ and $A = 1$,

$$1 = \tfrac{1}{2}(\theta - \sin\theta)$$

$$\therefore \quad 2 = \theta - \sin\theta$$

$$\theta - \sin\theta - 2 = 0$$

This is correct, for full marks.

(c) $f(2) = 2 - \sin 2 - 2 = -0.909$

$f(3) = 3 - \sin 3 - 2 = 0.8588$

Because there is a change of sign there must be a root α such that $f(\alpha) = 0$ and $2 < \alpha < 3$.

This is a correct and full explanation, for 3 marks.

(d) The Newton–Raphson formula is

$$x_{r+1} = x_r - \frac{f(x_r)}{f'(x_r)}$$

If $f(x) = x - \sin x - 2$ then $f'(x) = 1 - \cos x$. This gives

$$x_{r+1} = x_r - \frac{x_r - \sin x_r - 2}{1 - \cos x_r}$$

If $x_0 = 2$ then $x_1 = 2.642092616$, $x_2 = 2.555233541$, $x_3 = 2.554196115$, $x_4 = 2.554195953$.

Therefore, $\alpha = 2.554$ to 3 d.p.

This is correct and well presented, for 5 marks.

Question 3

The root of the equation

$$x^2 - \ln x - 2 = 0$$

is to be estimated using the iterative formula

$$x_{r+1} = (2 + \ln x_r)^{\frac{1}{2}}$$

(a) Show how the iterative formula is derived from the given equation. (2 marks)

(b) Given that the root lies between 1 and 2, use the iterative formula to find the root, correct to four decimal places. Write down all intermediate values generated by the iterative formula. (4 marks)

■ ■ ■

Answer to Question 3: candidate A (3 out of 6 marks)

(a) $x^2 - \ln x - 2 = 0$

$\therefore \quad x^2 = \ln x + 2$

$\therefore \quad x = \pm\ (\ln x + 2)^{\frac{1}{2}}$

The one we want is $x_{r+1} = +(\ln x_r + 2)^{\frac{1}{2}}$, as given in the question.

This is correct, for 2 marks.

(b) Let $x = 1$ and this gives error. Let $x = 2$, then the root is 1.5644.

This gains 1 mark for the initial value, $x = 2$, but nothing else. This candidate has ignored the instruction to write down all the intermediate generated values. The final answer is also incorrect because it has not been rounded.

■ ■ ■

Answer to Question 3: candidate B (5 out of 6 marks)

(a) $x^2 - \ln x - 2 = 0$

$\therefore \quad x^2 = \ln x + 2$

$\therefore \quad x = (\ln x + 2)^{\frac{1}{2}}$

This is correct, but lacks some commentary. For example, the final line gives one possible form for x but there is also the negative form, which is not mentioned. A final line showing x_r would be useful. This is awarded 1 mark out of 2.

(b) Let $x_0 = 2$, then $x_1 = 1.6410811$, $x_2 = 1.5796693$, $x_3 = 1.5675508$, $x_4 = 1.5650924$, $x_5 = 1.5645909$, $x_6 = 1.5644885$, $x_7 = 1.5644676$

The root is 1.5645 to 4 d.p.

This is correct, for 4 marks.

Question 4

Use the trapezium rule with five ordinates and interval width 0.25 to find an approximation of the definite integral

$$\int_1^2 \ln(1 + x^2)\,dx$$

Give your answer to three decimal places. (5 marks)

■ ■ ■

Answer to Question 4: candidate A (3 out of 5 marks)

x	1	1.25	1.5	1.75	2
$\ln(1 + x^2)$	0.693	0.811	0.916	1.012	1.099

Although this candidate has divided the interval [1, 2] correctly, the evaluation of $\ln(1 + x^2)$ for $x = 1.25$, 1.5, 1.75 and 2 is not correct. The candidate has not squared the x value before adding 1. The table gains 1 mark for the correct x values.

The approximate answer is

$$\frac{0.25}{2}\Big(0.693 + 2\,(0.811 + 0.916 + 1.012) + 1.099\Big) = 0.566$$

e Use of the trapezium rule is correct using the candidate's incorrect values, but the final answer is incorrect for these values. It seems that the candidate has not multiplied the sum of the middle three values by 2. This gains 2 of the 3 marks available.

■ ■ ■

Answer to Question 4: candidate B (5 out of 5 marks)

x	1	1.25	1.5	1.75	2
$\ln(1+x^2)$	0.6931	0.9410	1.1787	1.4018	1.6094

The approximate answer is

$$\frac{0.25}{2}\left(0.6931 + 2(0.9410 + 1.1787 + 1.4018) + 1.6094\right) = 1.168 \text{ to 3 d.p.}$$

e This is correct, for full marks.

Section 10

Vectors

Question 1

The lines L_1 and L_2 are given by the vector equations

$$\mathbf{r} = \begin{pmatrix} 1 \\ 0 \\ 2 \end{pmatrix} + t\begin{pmatrix} 0 \\ 3 \\ -1 \end{pmatrix} \quad \text{and} \quad \mathbf{r} = \begin{pmatrix} 1 \\ 1 \\ -1 \end{pmatrix} + s\begin{pmatrix} 0 \\ -7 \\ 5 \end{pmatrix}$$

respectively, where t and s are parameters.

(a) Show that L_1 and L_2 intersect at a point in the plane π given by

$$\mathbf{r}.\begin{pmatrix} 2 \\ -1 \\ 1 \end{pmatrix} = 12$$

(6 marks)

(b) Find the angle between the line L_2 and the plane π. (4 marks)

■ ■ ■

Answer to Question 1: candidate A (6 out of 10 marks)

(a)

$$\begin{pmatrix} 1 \\ 3t \\ 2-t \end{pmatrix} = \begin{pmatrix} 1 \\ 1-7s \\ -1+5s \end{pmatrix}$$

This gives $1 = 1$, $3t = 1 - 7s$ and $2 - t = -1 + 5s$.

Substitute $t = \dfrac{1-7s}{3}$ giving

$$2 - \frac{1-7s}{3} = -1 + 5s$$

$$6 - 1 - 7s = -1 + 5s$$

$$12s = 6$$

$$s = \tfrac{1}{2}$$

When $s = \frac{1}{2}$ the point is

$$\begin{pmatrix} 0 \\ -\frac{7}{2} \\ \frac{5}{2} \end{pmatrix}$$

To check if this point lies in the plane, substitute:

$$\begin{pmatrix} 0 \\ -\frac{7}{2} \\ \frac{5}{2} \end{pmatrix} \cdot \begin{pmatrix} 2 \\ -1 \\ 1 \end{pmatrix} = 0 + \frac{7}{2} + \frac{5}{2} = 6$$

e The first line of working is correct and the derived equations in t and s are also correct. This gains 2 marks. However, this candidate then makes a poor choice of equation to rearrange, as the resulting form involves a fraction, i.e. $t = \frac{1-7s}{3}$. The candidate then makes an error when multiplying through by 3, forgetting to multiply all terms on the right-hand side. No marks are awarded for s. However, the method to show that the point lies in the plane is correct and gains 1 mark, even though the candidate's point $(0, -\frac{7}{2}, \frac{5}{2})$ does not belong to the plane (he/she should have noticed this as the dot product gave 6 rather than 12).

(b) To find the angle,

$$\begin{pmatrix} 0 \\ -7 \\ 5 \end{pmatrix} \cdot \begin{pmatrix} 2 \\ -1 \\ 1 \end{pmatrix} = 0 + 7 + 5 = 12$$

Therefore,

$$12 = \sqrt{0 + 49 + 25}\sqrt{4 + 1 + 1}\cos\theta$$

$$\cos\theta = 0.569$$

$$\theta = 55.3°$$

e Here the candidate makes the right choice of direction vectors but forgets that the vector

$$\begin{pmatrix} 2 \\ -1 \\ 1 \end{pmatrix}$$

is perpendicular to the plane. The final angle of 55.3° needs to be subtracted from 90°. 3 marks are awarded.

■ ■ ■

Answer to Question 1: candidate B (8 out of 10 marks)

(a) At the intersection,

$$\begin{pmatrix} 1 \\ 3t \\ 2 - t \end{pmatrix} = \begin{pmatrix} 1 \\ 1 - 7s \\ -1 + 5s \end{pmatrix}$$

This gives $3t = 1 - 7s$ and $2 - t = -1 + 5s \Rightarrow t = 3 - 5s$.

Substituting $t = 3 - 5s$ into $3t = 1 - 7s$ gives

$$3(3 - 5s) = 1 - 7s$$

$$\therefore \quad 9 - 15s = 1 - 7s$$

$$\therefore \quad 8s = 8$$

$$\therefore \quad s = 1$$

When $s = 1$

$$\mathbf{r} = \begin{pmatrix} 1 \\ -6 \\ 4 \end{pmatrix}$$

The point of intersection is $(1, -6, 4)$. Substituting this into the equation of the plane:

$$\begin{pmatrix} 1 \\ -6 \\ 4 \end{pmatrix} \cdot \begin{pmatrix} 2 \\ -1 \\ 1 \end{pmatrix} = 2 + 6 + 4 = 12$$

Therefore, this point is in the plane π.

e This is correct, for 6 marks.

(b) The direction vector of L_2 is $\begin{pmatrix} 0 \\ -7 \\ 5 \end{pmatrix}$. The direction of the plane is $\begin{pmatrix} 2 \\ -1 \\ 1 \end{pmatrix}$.

The angle between them is given by

$$0 + 7 + 5 = \sqrt{74}\sqrt{6}\cos\theta$$

$$\theta = 55.28°$$

e The candidate states that the direction of the plane is given by the vector

$$\begin{pmatrix} 2 \\ -1 \\ 1 \end{pmatrix}$$

which is incorrect, as this vector is perpendicular to the plane. The angle θ determined by the candidate needs to be subtracted from 90°. The required angle is $90 - 55.28 = 34.72°$. 2 marks are awarded: 1 mark for calculating the dot product (even though one of the vectors being used was incorrect) and 1 mark for calculating θ.

Question 2

The line l has the vector equation

$$\mathbf{r} = \begin{pmatrix} 1 \\ 0 \\ 2 \end{pmatrix} + \mu \begin{pmatrix} 1 \\ -1 \\ 2 \end{pmatrix}$$

and the point A has coordinates (10, −1, 6).

(a) Find a vector equation for the line m, which passes through A and which is perpendicular to l. (5 marks)

(b) Find the coordinates of the point of intersection of the lines l and m. (4 marks)

(c) Calculate the perpendicular distance from the point A to the line l. (2 marks)

■ ■ ■

Answer to Question 2: candidate A (4 out of 11 marks)

(a) The line m is

$$\mathbf{r} = \begin{pmatrix} 10 \\ -1 \\ 6 \end{pmatrix} + t \begin{pmatrix} a \\ b \\ c \end{pmatrix}$$

and

$$\begin{pmatrix} a \\ b \\ c \end{pmatrix} \cdot \begin{pmatrix} 1 \\ 0 \\ 2 \end{pmatrix} = 0 \text{ because } l \text{ and } m \text{ are perpendicular.}$$

This means that a could be 1, b could be 0 and c could be $-\frac{1}{2}$.

ⓔ The first vector equation for the line m involving a, b and c gains 1 mark. The candidate then uses the incorrect vector from the equation of l to calculate the scalar product with

$$\begin{pmatrix} a \\ b \\ c \end{pmatrix}$$

The vector

$$\begin{pmatrix} 1 \\ 0 \\ 2 \end{pmatrix}$$

is merely the position vector of a point that the line l passes through and not the direction of the line. However, the method of using the scalar product is correct and gains a second mark.

(b) Intersection:

$$\begin{pmatrix}10\\-1\\6\end{pmatrix}+t\begin{pmatrix}1\\0\\-\frac{1}{2}\end{pmatrix}=\begin{pmatrix}1\\0\\2\end{pmatrix}+\mu\begin{pmatrix}1\\-1\\2\end{pmatrix}$$

$$10+t=1+\mu$$

$$-1=-\mu$$

$$6-\tfrac{1}{2}t=2+2\mu$$

This gives $\mu = 1$, so $10 + t = 1 + 1 \Rightarrow t = -8$.

e The method used to find the intersection is correct and gains 1 mark. The candidate does not check that the values for μ and t satisfy the third equation. A quick check by substituting would show they do not and that something has gone wrong.

(c) Point A is $(10, -1, 6)$ and the distance required is

$$\sqrt{(10-x)^2+(-1-y)^2+(6-z)^2}$$

e The candidate uses the correct formula but has not used the intersection point on l. The method gains 1 mark.

■ ■ ■

Answer to Question 2: candidate B (11 out of 11 marks)

(a) The line m is

$$\mathbf{r}=\begin{pmatrix}10\\-1\\6\end{pmatrix}+\lambda\begin{pmatrix}a\\b\\c\end{pmatrix}$$

If this is perpendicular to l, then the direction vectors of both lines will be perpendicular,

i.e. $\begin{pmatrix}1\\-1\\2\end{pmatrix}\cdot\begin{pmatrix}a\\b\\c\end{pmatrix}=0$

$$a-b+2c=0$$

Let $a = 3$, $b = 1$, then $c = -1$. This gives

$$m:\mathbf{r}=\begin{pmatrix}10\\-1\\6\end{pmatrix}+\lambda\begin{pmatrix}3\\1\\-1\end{pmatrix}$$

This is correct, for 5 marks. Notice that when the candidate derives the equation $a - b + 2c = 0$, the values chosen for a and b are carefully chosen to ensure that the c value is an integer (whole number). Any two of the three variables (a, b, c) could have been given values to determine the third.

(b) At intersection,

$$\begin{pmatrix} 10 \\ -1 \\ 6 \end{pmatrix} + \lambda \begin{pmatrix} 3 \\ 1 \\ -1 \end{pmatrix} = \begin{pmatrix} 1 \\ 0 \\ 2 \end{pmatrix} + \mu \begin{pmatrix} 1 \\ -1 \\ 2 \end{pmatrix}$$

$$10 + 3\lambda = 1 + \mu \quad (1)$$

$$-1 + \lambda = -\mu \quad (2)$$

$$6 - \lambda = 2 + 2\mu \quad (3)$$

From equation (2), $\lambda = 1 - \mu$.

Substituting in (1)

$$10 + 3(1 - \mu) = 1 + \mu$$

$$\therefore \quad 13 - 3\mu = 1 + \mu$$

$$\therefore \quad 4\mu = 12$$

$$\therefore \quad \mu = 3$$

This gives the intersection as

$$\mathbf{r} = \begin{pmatrix} 1 \\ 0 \\ 2 \end{pmatrix} + 3 \begin{pmatrix} 1 \\ -1 \\ 2 \end{pmatrix}$$

$$= \begin{pmatrix} 4 \\ -3 \\ 8 \end{pmatrix}$$

This is correct, for 4 marks.

(c) The distance between A (10, −1, 6) and B (4, −3, 8) is

$$d = \sqrt{(10 - 4)^2 + (-1 + 3)^2 + (6 - 8)^2}$$

$$= \sqrt{44}$$

This is correct, for 2 marks.